5 Elements of Sound Healing

5 Elements of Sound Healing

The Art of Vibrational Medicine and Sonic Ceremony

Bodhi Starwater

Crystal Wind Publishing

2023

5 Elements of Sound Healing: The Art of Vibrational Medicine and Sonic Ceremony

Crystal Wind Publishing
P.O. Box 1283
Mt. Shasta, CA 96067

soundscapeoasis.com
ksetchko@yahoo.com

1st Printing 2023
ISBN: 978-0-9973404-5-7

Author: Bodhi Starwater Setchko
Graphics layout: Brad Reynolds integralartandstudies.com
Front Cover design by: Murshidi Mahmud
Author photo and instrument photos by: Jasper Crocker

5 Elements of Sound Healing

The Art of Vibrational Medicine and Sonic Ceremony

Dedicated to

Tito La Rosa
Maestro Curandero de Sonido

who awakened in me
what I already knew was sleeping inside

SOUND

How to tame down this force of life
To narrow down with words
This potent vibrational field
That we inhabit as it lives within us

Take in these hieroglyphs
Like a breath of wind
Dancing through the space in between
In and around each sound

Savor these words slowly
Like a long, cool, drink of water
Refreshing your quantum sonic field
Relaxing the parasympathetic nervous system

I gently invite you to enter this portal

Breathe

Relax into the one sound
You are welcome here
The breath of life flows through us all
You are home

— Bodhi Starwater

Contents

Foreword

by Christine Stevens MSW, MT-BC

I was on a 40-day retreat in the Joshua Tree desert when I first heard Bodhi's acclaimed meditation music album, *Shamanic Flute*. A friend gifted me the CD because he had seen Bodhi perform at a personal growth event. He simply said, "this guy is amazing—it will help you."

During my time of solitude, the music created a soothing soundscape, a palette of slowing down, setting a field of beauty within and without. Titles like "Peace," "Birth," "Illumination," "Mystic Path" and "Reflection," gave me a transmission of these states of mind and heart. I could feel the intention of each track, reflecting my inner desire. Melodies seemed to float like petals carried by the wind through a deep canyon. In the pause, I breathed more deeply, and relaxed tense muscles in my jaw and neck. The sound seeped inward, an invitation to be with the softness of my interior call. As Sufi poet Kabir says, "The flute of the Infinite is played without ceasing and its sound is love."

I had become burned out living in the suburbs of Los Angeles. Although my work was rewarding, I knew it wasn't sustainable for my Nature-loving, awakening heart. Something had to change. As I sat in the desert, Bodhi's flute playing became the nectar of restoration I was deeply craving. No words could heal me; no food; no yoga posture. His sound was the salve that carried me to my own inner wisdom. After that retreat, I left Los Angeles and moved to Encinitas where I found a sacred sound community of Kirtan leaders, energy healers and sound bath practitioners, and felt at home.

Years later, Bodhi was invited to be a presenter for the Shift Network Global Sound Healing Summit and I was assigned to interview him. Imagine my surprise when I discovered he was the artist whose music so beautifully held me during my retreat and served as sound medicine for my out of tune soul. When synchronicity happens, beyond coincidence, you know something purposeful is awakening in your life. It's the mark of truth, the sonic imprint of an inner desire for transformation. Sound shows up when we are transforming as individuals, as humans: *homo-musicalis*.

People claim that the field of sound healing is the next big thing in the healing arts. Yet, it's not new. An ancient flute found in a German cave, dates back 35,000 years. Carved from bird bone, the three holes are spaced in similar distance as Indigenous clay flutes from South America, cedar flutes of First Nations, and bamboo flutes of Japan, India and Tibet. There is a universal scale marked by the distance between notes. As Bodhi will show you, the flute is a powerful instrument creating shifts in consciousness. Of the many instruments Bodhi plays in a sound healing experience, (including drums, rattles, guitar, voice, and bowls), when he brings in the flute, I feel the greatest invitation to journey and heal.

How does sound shift our energy: body, mind, and spirit? These insights into the practice of sound healing are the gift of Bodhi's knowledge, studies, and his personal work as a musician and shamanic flute player. I have learned from him the value of quality sound and how to play with intention, as an expression of universal feeling tones that transcend language. From his years of experience performing, recording, and leading sound healing sessions, as well as creating a sound healing temple in Mount Shasta, he brings an integrated and profound offering of knowledge to this growing field.

In this book, Bodhi gives us a guide to stepping into one of the most powerful and ancient methods of spiritual awakening, healing, and transformation known to humanity. We are given a compass, a map for a voyage into the world of sound healing tools, to guide our way toward inner healing and leading sound sessions for groups and individuals. We will dive deeply into the five elements and their sound correlations, understand sacred instruments, their cultural origin, and gifts. It offers a methodology based on traditional teachers from a South American lineage, deep musical explorations and Bodhi's many years in the trenches of human transformation. Through its reading, we enter a space that holds opposites: science and spirit; sound and silence; practical and mystical; self and world. This is the gift of the medicine wheel, the mandala, and the map Bodhi offers us to explore sound as musicians, healers, energy workers, coaches, spiritual leaders, and ones who love music.

Whatever brought this book into your life, like the way Bodhi's music found me, it is divine timing for you and delivers a potent message. Sound healing is a calling to be of service to self and humanity, uplifting the frequency of all beings. As Nigerian drum master Babatunde Olatunji said, "There should be a drum in every household." Perhaps then, we shall become an enlightened world. Get your drum, flute, strings, bowls, rattles, and silence…let your journey begin.

Christine Stevens
2023 Jackson Hole, WY

Instrument Mesa

How To Use This Book

Start anywhere and jump in. Or read it from cover to cover. It's an infinite loop with no beginning and no end. The Path of Sound Healing is ever-expanding and ever-awakening. Go where you are drawn and find your own way to begin absorbing the sonic medicine that is all around us. There are many treasures along the path. Learn to surf the waves of sound and consciousness as you deepen your understanding and practical application of the art of vibrational medicine and sonic ceremony. There are a few blank pages at the end of the book to write your visions, revelations and insights.

Introduction

Silence is the mother of all sound.
– Tito La Rosa

The aim and final end of all music
should be none other than the glory of God
and the refreshment of the soul.
– Johann Sebastian Bach

Missing Only One Sound

"Falta solamente uno sonido." You are missing only one sound. That was all he said after three hours together. Tito has a way of getting to the point.

He disappeared into another room and came back with the Mama Quena, a deep bamboo flute from Peru, very similar to the Shakuhachi from Japan. I cringed. I had avoided playing this kind of flute my whole life. "It's too hard. I don't want to do this," I thought to myself. The resistance began to melt as my teacher gently provoked me. "You're a musician, learn it," he said with a smile.

Mama Quena came home with me. No matter from whatever angle I approached her with, she wouldn't sing to me. It was like being underwater. My lungs were empty from blowing so much.

One day, the faintest sound emerged. I held the tone as best I could. Tentatively, I slid my fingers over the holes, but all I heard was my breath. At first I couldn't shake the heat of frustration. But it grew into a devoted obsession. I had to learn this. Mama Quena was slowly seducing me.

Two years flew by. Tito was teaching for a small group of students in Peru. I was living in a tipi, close to the elements. The class setting was magnificent; a beautiful large round structure filled with windows around the perimeter. Flowers bloomed in radiant colors. Majestic white clouds drifted through the blue, Sacred Valley skies, carried by a warm, gentle breeze. The Mama Quena sang clear and true as Tito played with the practiced grace of a master.

As he passed by me, he picked up another Quena and placed it in my hands. Slowly, I stood. Wild thoughts sailed through my mind and it felt like I was underwater again. Lifting the flute to my lips, I left my body. I was looking down on myself playing with him.

Far off, I heard the wind soughing through the tree tops. I opened my eyes and was back in the room. We had become one melody, the one sound I was missing.

Sound is a living organism, a sonic language. Just as sounds fade, these words evaporate, dissolving like disappearing ink moments after they are written or spoken out loud. Nothing lasts forever, everything is constantly changing. Like William Blake said, "We kiss the joy as it flies by."

Sound healing has always been a part of my musical path. When I was fourteen, I heard Paul Horn play his flute in the Taj Mahal on an album called *Inside*. I listened to this album over and over with my headphones and went into a mystical dreamspace. This experience awakened in me the magical power of the flute and I purchased my first silver flute.

When I was very young, I remember that people felt good after hearing music. I would play the guitar, flute, or the piano and people would get happy, and then I got happy. I thought, "This is a quick path to happiness!" I knew then that I wanted to be a musician. I stayed with it and gradually added many different instruments to my orchestra as I evolved and discovered new sounds.

Every sound has a unique vibration and frequency, creating the soundtrack of our lives. The more ways we choose to orchestrate that symphony, the more ways we can balance our lives. Sound can be used to heal the body, calm the mind, and uplift the spirit. The principles of sound healing are rooted in the understanding that everything in the universe is in a state of vibration, including our bodies. When we are out of balance and experience dis-ease, it can manifest in physical, emotional, or spiritual symptoms. Sound healing works by using the space of silence and the vibration of love restoring balance and harmony to our bodies.

After years of studying with many different teachers and artists, I have fully embraced Nature as my music teacher. I find my greatest solace in the creeks, the crickets, the birds, the frogs, the ocean, and the wind in the trees. I spend a lot of time listening. The silence in between the sounds is also a very special place, a place of peace and tranquility. In fact, the silence IS a sound.

Have you noticed that you feel better when you take a walk in a natural place, listening to the wind or the water, absorbing the sunlight and dancing on the earth? This is because natural sounds are what our bodies are attuned to. In essence, it's what we are. The next time you're outside, take time to pause and listen. You will start to feel and hear the melodies of nature, tuning into the rhythms of life.

The Sound Healing practice I employ starts with nature,

with natural sounds. In a sound healing session, the sounds of the instruments are effectively re-creating the vibrations of nature, which helps us to relax, allowing the body's natural healing systems to recalibrate our being. It's a simple practice and non-invasive. It has the potential to help calm frenetic energy that gets built up with fear and dis-ease.

This practice has affected how I play music. I play more simply, play less notes, tuning in to what each note is creating and the effect it has on me and the listener. There is a resonance that happens when we create sounds that are in tune with nature. When you are working with pure sound, you're not evoking feelings or memories from the past. Instead, you are inviting your True Nature to be present; you're invoking a "here and now" experience.

If a sound is familiar, like listening to a song from your childhood, your mind might go to the place where you first heard that song. It might remind you of a person or a place and brings up a feeling in your body. The whole point of sound healing is to channel vibrations that awaken us to THIS moment, to relax and align the energies within our body. Many people find that by soothing the mind and body with harmonious sound, it is much easier to drop into a meditative state.

I consider sound healing to be sonic nourishment, keeping your body healthy with preventative care. It has been used for thousands of years across cultures and traditions to promote physical, emotional, and spiritual wellbeing. During a sound healing experience, you may go on a journey, seeing visions of animals and colors. Others simply fall asleep and allow the frequencies to work on them while their body rests. Osho says, "Relaxation can transform you to such beautiful heights; it will bring new light to your eyes, a new freshness to your being, and it will help you understand what meditation is. It is just the first step outside the door of the temple of meditation.

With deeper and deeper relaxation, it becomes meditation."

In this book, I share my own journey of discovering the power of sound and the techniques that have worked for me. We are seeking to understand, with words and form, the power of intentional sound. By working with the 5 elements and the principles of sound healing, we can learn to create powerful, transformative experiences that help us to align with our true nature. I also provide practical guidance on how to choose and use different sound healing instruments, and how to create a sound healing session.

I have drawn from many traditions, mostly from the perspective of the intuitive schools, to weave a unique blend of sound healing practices. The scientific schools also have a deep place in the sound healing field and I have learned from these as well. In a sense, this re-mix becomes something I have created, knowing I am connected to the source, the same source these traditions were born from. Evolution is a constantly morphing process. Culture is created relative to where we live and what we experience.

As you read these words, you might choose to speak them aloud to awaken their meaning. Words can never capture the full spectrum of the reality we inhabit. Move your body, dance your dream, and awaken your inner Sound Healer. As I like to say, "Life works better when we are 'in tune'."

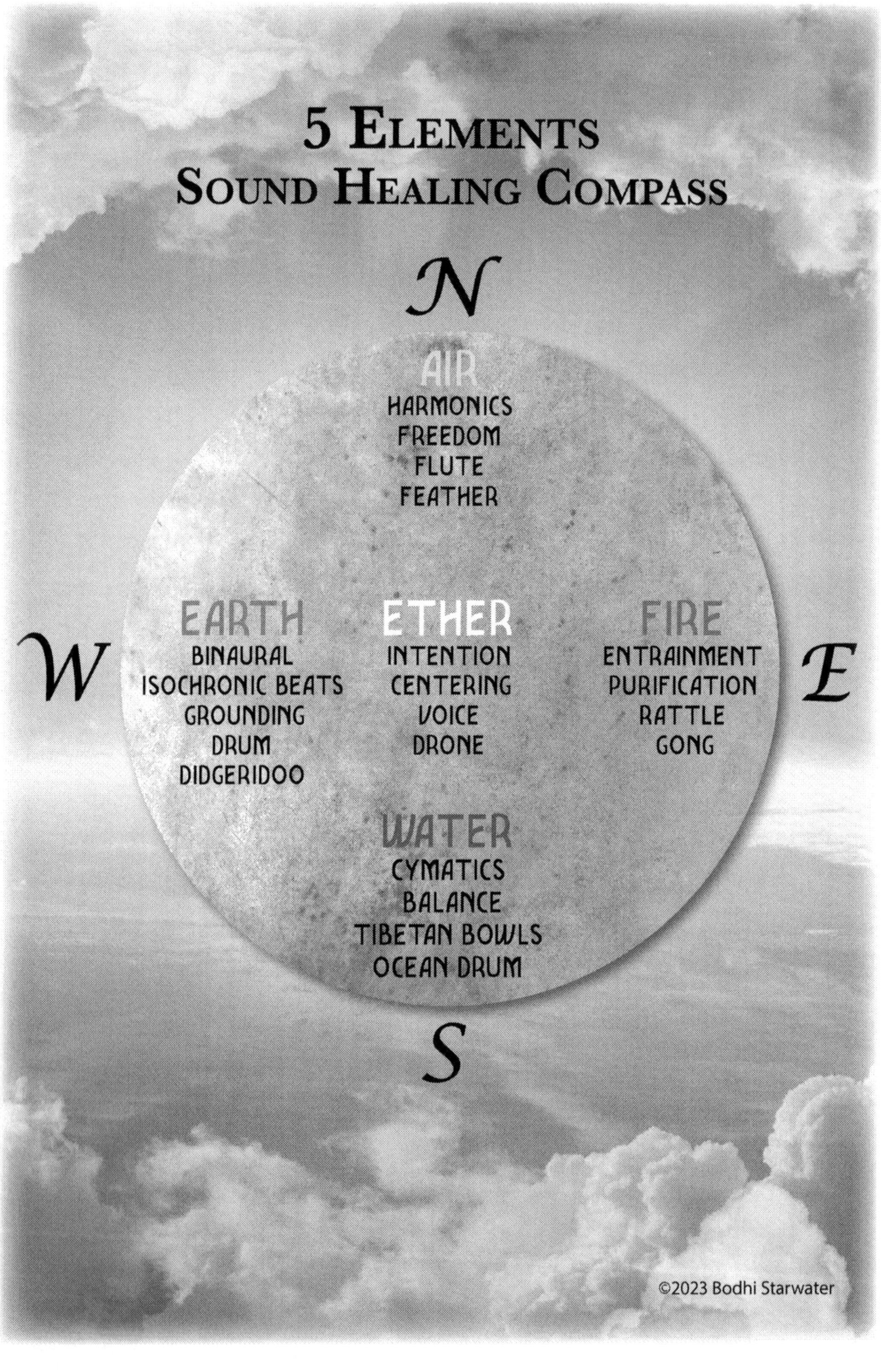

5 Elements
Sound Healing Compass

N

AIR
HARMONICS
FREEDOM
FLUTE
FEATHER

W

EARTH
BINAURAL
ISOCHRONIC BEATS
GROUNDING
DRUM
DIDGERIDOO

ETHER
INTENTION
CENTERING
VOICE
DRONE

FIRE
ENTRAINMENT
PURIFICATION
RATTLE
GONG

E

WATER
CYMATICS
BALANCE
TIBETAN BOWLS
OCEAN DRUM

S

1

The 5 Elements

Sound is the force of creation, the true whole.
Music then becomes the voice of the great cosmic oneness
and therefore the optimal way to reach this final state of healing.

— Hazrat Inayat Khan

Coals of the Fire

Ten thousand feet up, in the mountains of Northern India, the cold night stood still around me. I was sitting alone in a cave. The distant lights of an entire city danced in my eyes from the shimmering coals of the fire, while Sadhus across the canyon cried out, "Bom Bholenath!" a call out to honor Lord Shiva.

I could hear the rush of water over rocks from the river that tumbled through the valley. Amidst the roaring melody, the rhythm of crackling fire could be heard. The fragrance of the wild forest, woodsmoke, chillum tobacco, and lit incense surrounded me. The moist taste of high altitude air filled my mouth like a sip of iced pine needle tea. All around me, the elements gathered.

This was the music of my soul. My mind and body relaxed completely. Like a bird gliding in the wind, I was soaring. The elemental choir resounded in my consciousness while I traveled through different portals. Like a cup overflowing with water, gratitude brimmed in my heart. These were the purest sounds on earth. Through their intimate presence, the elements sang to me and my trust in their teaching deepened. I surrendered to their wisdom.

Everything vibrates within the quantum field of our reality. The five elements of nature, Ether, Fire, Water, Earth, and Air, are the building blocks of our universe. We live in this world of elements and the way they interact is how we exist. Understanding the nature of these elements helps us to navigate our world. They mix and remix, constantly rearranging in new patterns. Fire and Water create steam, Water and Earth make mud. Fire needs Air to burn, Fire and Earth create pottery. Air and Water become floating clouds.

We instinctively know whatever we need to know, at any time and place. Life is an ever-changing dynamic of motion, harmony and balance. Everything that exists has a vibrational frequency. When we align ourselves with harmonious frequencies, we feel at ease and peaceful.

In this book, I have applied the elements to the practice of sound healing. Each element has its own unique properties and can be used to promote healing in different ways. We allow the elements to teach us. To live in harmony with nature, we learn to balance the elements within our body and being; a fluid dance of vibrational freedom.

Although I have associated each element with a sound healing principle, a quality and an instrument, in reality, all the elements overlap and interact freely. The instruments I have chosen to represent each element have multiple aspects of all of the elements. The same applies to the qualities and the principles. Knowing this, we start from somewhere and expand our awareness as we grow and learn. Life is a holistic experience, not confined to any one box.

Elements

ETHER, also known as Space or Akasha, is the most subtle of the five elements. It is used in sound healing to create a sense of spaciousness and clarity.

FIRE represents transformation and purification. A powerful element used to create energy, movement, clearing and release in a sound healing session.

WATER represents fluidity and flow. It is a gentle element used to promote emotional healing and relaxation.

EARTH represents stability and grounding, bringing a sense of calm and presence.

AIR represents openness and expansiveness. This element evokes a sense of freedom and lightness of being.

Directions

ETHER – Inside

FIRE – East

WATER – South

EARTH – West

AIR – North

Sound Healing Principles

ETHER – Intention

FIRE – Entrainment

WATER – Cymatics

EARTH – Binaural and Isochronic beats

AIR – Harmonics

Qualities

ETHER – Centering

FIRE – Purification

WATER – Balance

EARTH – Grounding

AIR – Freedom

Instruments

ETHER – Voice & Drone

FIRE – Rattle & Gong

WATER – Tibetan and Crystal Bowls & Ocean Drum

EARTH – Drum & Didgeridoo

AIR – Flute & Feather

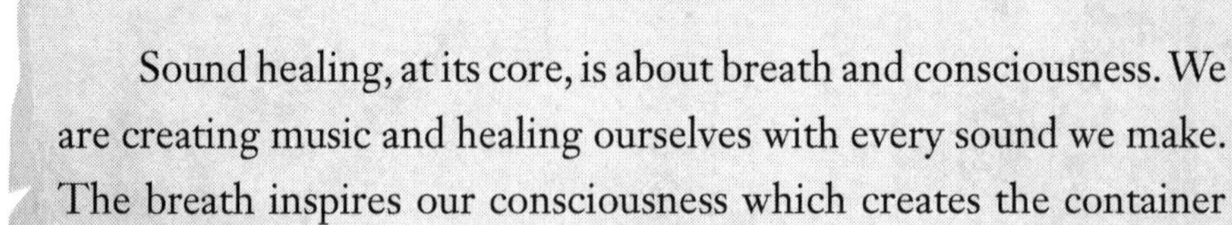

Sound healing, at its core, is about breath and consciousness. We are creating music and healing ourselves with every sound we make. The breath inspires our consciousness which creates the container where healing happens. If we align ourselves with this in every endeavor, life can be a blessing. Sacred space is created by intentional Ceremony and Ritual. All of life is sacred and by recognizing and honoring this, we open ourselves to divine guidance.

Sound Healing Table of 5 Elements

Element	Direction	Principle	Quality	Instrument
Ether	Inside	Intention	Centering	Voice Drone
Fire	East	Entrainment	Purification	Rattle Gong
Water	South	Cymatics	Balance	Tibetan Bowls Ocean Drum
Earth	West	Binaural Isochronic Beats	Grounding	Drum Didgeridoo
Air	North	Harmonics	Freedom	Flute Feather

2

Element of Ether

In our tradition, the inner world is called Uku Pacha. It's the center of everything, inside your body, inside your heart. I invite you to enter into your Uku Pacha, your inner world, the universe within, where you can see yourself and feel yourself in a deep way. Here you have an opportunity to create new possibilities in your life, a deeper connection with yourself, with a feeling of energy, Munay, which is the energy of love.

— Tito LaRosa

Breath sweeps mind.

— Roshi Kwong

Direction: Inside
Sound Healing Principle: Intention
Quality: Centering
Instruments: Voice & Drone

Finding My Voice

It was a moment in singing class that changed everything for me. Like many people, I hated my voice. I had taken voice lessons; I had sung to the wind and ocean; I had screamed into the heavens until my voice was hoarse and my throat dry. I had done everything possible to free my voice. After years, I still couldn't access my primordial instrument. Then, in a moment, it all opened up.

"Take a breath, and hold the note for as long as you can," our teacher instructed. I filled my lungs with air. Everyone started at once, "Ahhhhh..." Before my own intonation started, the teaching of ether came through me: *breath is the source*. I *felt* it, I *knew* it!

I breathed deeply into my belly. I felt the connection to my center. I kept expanding like an endless balloon. I began, quietly at first, "Ahhh..."

Slowly, inexorably I was filled with a new sense of gentle power. "AHHH..." My voice came through, clear and strong. I was actually singing freely! I felt like I could go on forever. Like a bird flying for the first time, I was soaring, liberated in ecstasy.

It all begins with the breath, allowing ourselves to open to what is natural inside of us all.

Element of Ether

We start in the center with the element of Ether. This is where we find our inner music. In this chapter, we will explore how to work with this element in the context of sound healing and how it can help us to connect with our inner wisdom and intuition. Ether is the element of space and infinite potential. It is the most subtle of the elements and represents the space in which all other elements exist. It has neither the movement of wind, the heat of fire, the coolness of water, nor the firmness of earth. It is "akasha," the sky: boundless, formless, completely free. Ether is the beginning of All, holds All together, and moves through All. It can help us to connect with our inner wisdom and intuition. It is here that all things begin and it is here that we begin our journey.

The element of Ether is often considered the space in which all of life exists. It represents the void or the space in which sound is transmitted. The throat and vocal cords are responsible for our ability to express ourselves and communicate through sound. Ether moves circularly and spirally. It is more of a felt sense as it does not have the qualities of the other earthly elements, like temperature or texture. The closest experience of Ether on this planet is light. Light is considered to be similar in quality to Ether.

Ether has the quality of centering. When we relax and open to this element, we tune into our own being and our own heart. This helps us to feel aligned with our True Self, the place in us that is calm and peaceful. When we tune into our heart-center and become aware of our breath, our breathing slows down, our heart rate slows down, the muscles in our face and bellies soften. It's easier to allow the corners of our mouth to curl up and the furrow in our brow to smooth. When we embrace the element of Ether, we feel the spaciousness and the expansiveness of our being.

Tuning in to the Element of Ether

Find a quiet place and tune into your inner self. Feel the stillness, silence is a sound. Become aware of your breath, relaxing into a natural rhythm. As you drop into meditation, you can consciously deepen your breath, gently expanding your diaphragm to allow the lungs to open and fill. Notice any sensations or insights that arise and just be with them. Stay with this practice as long as it is comfortable. We are beginning to develop a stronger sense of connection and trust with our own intuition.

Sound Healing Principle: Intention

Jonathan Goldman offers the simple formula: "Frequency plus

Intention equals Healing. If we can find the right sound frequency coupled with the right intention, then healing will occur."

Some definitions of intention are: "An anticipated outcome that is intended or that guides your planned actions: an act of intending; a volition that you intend to carry out. Synonyms: aim, design, intent, mission, purpose."

Having an intention is having a desire to perform a certain action and a belief that one will perform this action. We can use our free will to choose our thoughts. We have the power to intentionally think and influence our entire life with our mind. Every single person is using the power of intention in every moment of their lives, whether they are aware of it or not. Every time we think, we are intending our future life. We create our own future through the power of intention and utilizing this means deliberately thinking thoughts of the future we want.

When we are practicing the art of sound healing, we set a positive intention before every ceremony. It's very important to remember the power of our thoughts when working with the subtle realms of consciousness. Set an intention for the highest and best possible outcome for all concerned and our journeys will have the beneficial effect we are seeking.

History of the Voice and Drone

The Voice: Primordial Connection to Source

Ancient Indigenous cultures knew the power of the voice and used techniques of the breath to bring on altered states of consciousness and being, bridging the realms of the subconscious and conscious. In *The Roar of Silence* Don Campbell asserts, "The mystery schools of sound knew the vital importance of the connection between spirit and body. They used patterns of tone, movement, and breath to open the inner gates where awakened energy could flow between subconscious and conscious worlds." A study cited in *The Humming Effect* by Goldman & Goldman states that humming brings the body into a state of relaxation and receptivity.

Many breathing techniques commonly used today date back over 5 thousand years ago to ancient India, and come from the science of Ayurveda: Ujjayi, or Ocean's breath, Nadi Shodhana, or alternate nostril breathing, and Brahmari, or the humming breath are a few examples. All of these breathing techniques create sounds and bring on a state of relaxation. Through patterns of tone, movement, and breath, these cultures utilized various vocal techniques to open the inner gates, allowing awakened energy to flow freely.

The Drone: Bedrock of Meditation

A drone is the sound of one note or a chord being played in a continuous loop. Some examples of drones include the shruti box, didgeridoo, Tibetan singing bowls, the tamboura, the bagpipes, which contain three drones, and the banjo, whose last string is a drone string. Drone music, along with deep listening, has been used since ancient times to calm the central nervous system and induce states of deep relaxation, serving as a foundation for meditative experiences.

Technique

Your Voice

It all begins with the breath.

Find an upright posture, seated or standing. We begin with the Primordial Breath or the Buddha Breath. As we breathe in, the diaphragm presses down, allowing the lungs to fill with air as the belly, back, and sides expand outward. When we exhale, the belly pulls back in, pushing the air out of the lungs. Keep the neck and shoulders relaxed. Let the air pass freely through the throat, controlling the flow with the belly and diaphragm.

We start our sounding practice by breathing in through the nose, and releasing the breath through the mouth with a sighing "Oh"sound. Try playing with different vowel sounds: A-E-I-O-U. Draw them out and blend them together. Allow the sound to naturally arise from deep within. Next we can add some humming to this slow, rhythmic breathing and toning. Feel the resonance throughout your body. Stay with this simple practice for as long as it is comfortable.

This vocal toning practice can be complete by itself. It can also be a great warm-up for mantra chanting. Chanting is a very deep form of meditation and sound healing. The well known chants, OM and AUM are sacred sounds in Hinduism, Buddhism, and other Indian religions. Both represent universal vibrations and are used in meditation and religious rituals, fostering spiritual connection. OM is pronounced as "ohm", while AUM is pronounced as "Ah-oh-mmm". The language of sound is a universal healer. No matter if it's the blues, icaros, mantra, hymns, or a lullaby to a baby, singing is a healing balm. The more we train our voice to open and express itself freely, the more completely we can surrender to the Divine in our singing

Toning is a practice of using vibration to nourish the cells of the body, aligning with our own true nature. We can do an internal vibrational sound healing any time with our own voice. Experimenting with these different vocal tones might sound silly at first. Just let go and have fun with it. If you start to feel light-headed, pause and take a break. With each day that you practice, your stamina and focus will grow.

Penelope

In a flash of golden light, I knew my mother had passed.

I was watching the waves dance on the beach at high noon, each silvery crest sparkled with a brilliance I had never seen before. At that moment, I felt within my whole being the ethereal connection that is possible between humans who love each other. I began to cry and hum and felt the emptiness of the space she had filled in my life. At the same time, I experienced a transcendent timelessness and freedom.

I had spent the night before singing and playing music for her. She loved to sing and helped me to open my voice when I was young. Now she would always be with me. All I need to do is sing to her and invite her presence.

We are all connected through the Ether-net.

Invitation to Practice

Become present. Feel into the element of Ether and allow it to tune you. Find a quiet place to sit in silence and listen. Find your inner stillness. Set an intention that aligns with your personal well-being. If you like, use some sort of drone sound to establish a tonal center.

Start humming and feel the inner resonance in your body. Feel the immediate effects and allow yourself to be nurtured by your own voice. When you hum, you are effectively hearing the echo of your breath as it strikes your sound chords. Humming allows you to tune into your body's own natural frequency and centers you into your being.

Resonance is the vibration that is created when breath moves through the vocal cords, like when a guitar string is plucked. Resonance comes from the Latin word *resonare* which means "to resound" or *resonantia* meaning "an echo." You can easily experience this by singing in the shower. Play with your voice up and down, high and low until the chamber awakens in resonance. You will feel and hear it!

Start with a few minutes a day and expand it over time as your stamina increases. At some point, you might want to add an instrument, like a drum or a rattle. Enjoy the process of awakening your voice.

3

Element of Fire

Through the process of entrainment, sound can transform negative, repressed emotions into a state of psychological equanimity that has direct and immediate effects on our physiology. Sonic entrainment can also restore harmony between our innermost selves, our essence, and the universe, thus awakening our spirit connection.

— Mitchell Gaynor, M.D.
The Healing Power of Sound

Direction: East
Sound Healing Principle: Entrainment
Quality: Purification
Instruments: Rattle & Gong

The Rattle

What does it feel like to go into a trance? For me, it feels comforting, like a deep rest; a complete letting go of everything. It was many years ago that I first experienced the power of the rattle to invoke trance.

A shamanka from Siberia came to California to give a presentation. I still remember seeing her in the chair with that rattle, just one rattle. She began to play and continued for 45 minutes. The whole room was transfixed. The hypnotic tone led me into a deep journey. It started as just a sound in the room, then it became the sound of my consciousness, until it was only sound. The one sound. I opened up and let go of thinking. The limitations of my body and mind began to melt away.

I settled into myself completely and drifted inwards. I experienced a timeless zone, and the ease of accessing the wisdom that's in that place. It's the theta state of consciousness where one is unified with the quantum field. I could see everything all at once, it was perfect and joyful. I was surprised by how simple it is to be taken on a shamanic journey. With just one rattle, I learned how to bring others into a deep trance.

Element of Fire

We move to the East, the element of Fire, the place of the sunrise. Known as Grandfather Fire in the Huichol tradition, fire is the first healer. Fire is the element of transformation and purification. It represents the energy of change and the power of the sun.

The element of fire in sound healing can help us to release old patterns and beliefs that no longer serve us. It symbolizes death and transformation and opens the door for rebirth and renewal. It corresponds to vitality, courage, creativity, and motivation.

Through the use of instruments such as gongs and rattles, which have a strong percussive quality, the element of fire can be used to create energy and movement, purifying the container of our practice.

Tuning into the Element of Fire

Sit with a candle or around a campfire and tune into the pure, natural sound of the element itself. Listen to the crackling, the pop of wood exploding, and the hiss of water evaporating. There is a peaceful and tranquil experience of a single candle flame, burning bright in the darkness like a beacon of hope. Pay attention to any feelings that arise. The flame can be a powerful teacher.

Sound Healing Principle—Entrainment

In 1665, a Dutch scientist named Christian Huygens discovered the principle of entrainment. As it is employed in sound healing, entrainment is the coordination or synchronization of different rhythms, creating resonance. A few instruments that can induce entrainment are rattles, drums, feathers, or anything that creates a slow, consistent pulse. This helps the brain to slow down and relax using a rhythm that is similar to one of the states of deep brainwave consciousness, such as delta or theta. [See Appendix D for full-page Brain Wave States]

Brain Wave States	Brain Wave Frequencies	Qualities of Consciousness
Gamma	30 - 100 Hz	Insight, Peak Focus, Expanded Consciousness
Beta	13 - 30 Hz	Alertness, Concentration, Conscious thought, Stress, Anxiety, Cognition
Alpha	8 - 13 Hz	Light relaxation, Superlearning, Positive thinking, Visualization, Creativity
Theta	4 - 8 Hz	Deep relaxation, Meditation, Increased memory, Intuition, Focus, Dreams, REM sleep
Delta	.5 - 4 Hz	Deep sleep, Lucid dreaming, Healing, Increased immune functions

History of the Rattle and Gong

The Rattle: Power and Magic

The use of rattles is found in many cultures around the world. They have been used for thousands of years for various purposes, including shamanic entrainment. The rattling sound produced by a shaman's rattle serves several purposes beginning with putting the shaman into a trance-like state. They use rattles in rituals and ceremonies to create altered states of consciousness and are often used to mark transitions, invoke sacred space, and set the stage for healing work. The sound and vibration of the rattle are believed to have energetic qualities that can clear negative or stagnant energies and restore balance.

Priests and Priestesses in Ancient Egypt used rattles during funerary rites to call on the power of regeneration in the afterlife. The Indigenous people of the Northeastern United States used turtle shell rattles and the people of Amazonian Brazil, Africa, and Oceania have used rattles for healing and protection. Gourd and skin rattles are among the most common rattles used today.

Rattles, made of shells, bones, hooves, or seeds that have been strung together and tied in bunches, and attached to a dancer's body are among the earliest musical instruments, dating back to prehistoric times. These instruments are called slung rattles and are still used today in performances around the world.

Small objects enclosed in another object have long been used as protective charms and amulets; this is where the term "jingle bell" comes from. Bells, small beads and seeds, and other objects placed together to create a jingling or rattling sound have been used in dances, ceremonial rites, and on journeys to ensure protection and to create desired outcomes.

The Gong: Resonance and Harmonious Convergence

Gongs originated in East and Southeast Asia, most likely dating back to prehistoric times. Some of the earliest depictions of gongs can be seen in art from Vietnam. The ancient cultures of the Egyptians, Greeks, Romans, Persians, Mongols, and Uighers knew the power of gongs. Gongs were used in Ancient China for rituals and tribal meetings and to signify the coming and going of culturally significant figures; they have gradually found their way into healing practices.

In Chinese medicine, gongs are used to help clear blockages in the meridian system and promote the circulation of vital energy. Most gongs are made of bronze or brass, suspended in the air, and played with hammers or mallets. Each different mallet can evoke a unique and distinct sound from the gong and each has different healing effects. Gongs create waves of sound, much like the waves of the ocean, which allow people to enter deep states of presence and resonance, allowing the harmonious convergence of the physical, mental, and spiritual bodies to occur.

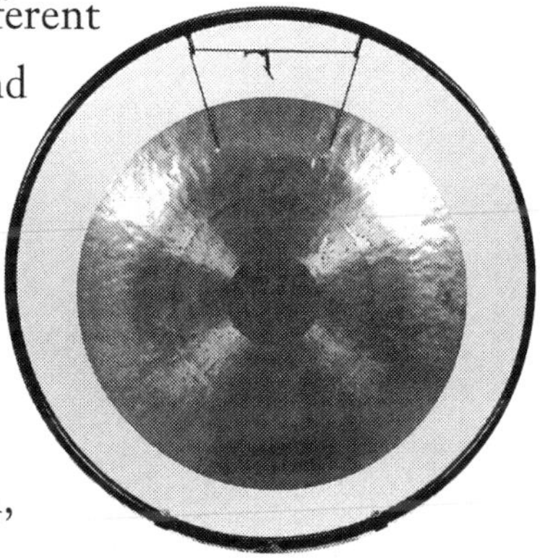

There are several types of gongs used today in orchestras, rock bands, and sound healing. They are also used in religious ceremonies and in the gamelan orchestras of Indonesia where the resonant sound invokes a spiritual presence and creates a sacred atmosphere. In contemporary sound healing practices, gong baths have become quite popular. Participants lie down or sit while a facilitator plays the gong and creates a meditative, sonic experience. The sustained vibrations and overtones produced by the gong can facilitate a state of expanded awareness, aiding in relaxation and the exploration of inner states of consciousness.

Technique

The Rattle

The rattle is one of the deepest trance instruments for me. It's such a gentle invocation to the journey. It's all about the steady rhythm and the accent. One stroke with the elbow, two strokes with the wrist with a fluid, relaxed motion. The most common accents would be on the "3" in a 4/4 time signature;

1 2 **3** 4

and the "2" & "4";

1 **2** 3 **4**

I often practice with a metronome (timekeeper) at 60 BPM (Beats per minute) to keep a steady tempo for the shamanic journey entrainment. Changing the accent and the tempo create variations in the mood. Keep your breath smooth and easy to enhance the experience.

Also, try shaking the rattle like a rattlesnake, a shaking motion in different areas around the body, near the heart, at the back of the neck, up and down the spine. Not too close, gently, gently, softly invoking. Respect the person's space, inviting the presence of healing in a natural, organic way.

The Gong

The gong is one of the most powerful and popular sound healing instruments. There are many types and sizes of gongs and each has its own character. Two popular sizes are 32 and 38 inches. The Paiste brand gong is quite beautiful and resonant for our purposes.

In general, the gong is used to clear the space, break up stuck energy and create a sonic universe all its own. There are many different types of mallets to excite the gong to life and every gong player has a distinctive style and technique for playing the instrument.

My favorite technique is to do a gentle, dynamic, swelling roll with two medium mallets. For about ten to twelve minutes, one can create a beautiful, mystical portal with the gong. Gently rising and falling like waves, ascending to a grand peak in the middle of the journey. As it fades away, you can bring in a softer metal sound like a Tibetan Bowl to exit the portal.

Another popular technique is to use small rubber mallets to rub the surface to create whale and dolphin like frequencies. These can be quite other-worldly sounding. The gong, with its myriad expressions, is a very versatile member of the sound healing orchestra.

Subtle Power

The sunlight gleaned from the instruments spread around the room. For nearly three hours I had been watching Tito intently. I studied how he held the flute and how he strummed the charango. I observed his movements as he flicked the feathers effortlessly. It was only the gong that lay untouched in the corner.

I had been to plenty of gong baths and had seen the way they were played. I appreciated the power of it but the prolonged thundering sometimes overwhelmed my senses. I wondered how Tito would strike the gong and how long he would hold the resonance. Like a spring bubbling up from the earth, curiosity rose in me. "How should we use the gong?" I asked him.

He looked at me and smiled. Without saying a word, he picked up the mallet. In what looked like a slow motion dance, he lightly struck the gong once. Putting the mallet down, he raised his hands and smiled again. I was spellbound. With just one strike, I understood the subtle power of the gong.

In Search of the Perfect Rattle: A Lifelong Journey

There's a certain feeling and balance of sound within a rattle that makes it the perfect vibrational companion. A rattle can help to bring us back to the present moment. Every rattle has its own voice and life force, and for those who choose to listen, each will speak to you. This is what makes them the perfect allies.

I have owned many rattles over the years—from plastic egg shakers to rocks in cans. I have some small woven basket shakers. The ones I love best were made by the man who tended the garden of Ram Dass. I acquired some bigger rattles made from deer skin recommended to me by my teacher, Tito. I decorated these with leather and wrapped threads. These rattles accompanied me to many sonic ceremonies over the years, yet I could still hear the distant call of another rattle in the future.

On my journey to visit Tito in Peru, I came upon a pair of the most beautiful rattles I had ever seen at the shaman's store in Urubamba. Adorned with feathers and a small stone each, they were made from goat skin. Fringe dangled just below the handle carved from palo santo wood. I picked one up. The feeling of it in my hand and the soft shaking sound that emanated told me everything I needed to know: these were the allies that had been calling me.

Invitation to Practice

Sit by a fire or candle and play the rattle. With an easy breath, stay relaxed and focused. Strive for consistency and endurance. You are developing an even and rhythmic sense of time. Practice with a metronome or play along with a recorded track of music if you want to challenge yourself to keep a steady rhythm over a long period of time. This can be very trance inducing. Enjoy the sensation of dropping into "the zone." Over time, you may find the rattle to be one of your favorite portals.

The gong is its own world altogether. Even a small gong can be a powerful portal when woven into a sonic ceremony. If you are fortunate enough to have a large gong, you can transport yourself and your audience on a very deep journey. Feel the fire of purification as you ride the swells of sound, swirling around the room and through your bodies. It does not have to be loud to be effective, especially in a smaller setting. I find a softer approach to be much more inviting. Feel into the space and find the appropriate level at which to work.

Fire to Water

4

Element of Water

The more one studies these things, the more one realizes that sound is the creative principle. It must be regarded as primordial.

— Hans Jenny

Direction: South
Sound Healing Principle: Cymatics
Quality: Balance
Instruments: Bowls & Ocean Drum

The Canyon Wren

Her cry was echoing off the canyon walls. I sat with my small, clay ocarina flute, silent in my hands, waiting for just the right moment to answer her call. I was transported to a field beyond time and space. A lightness started in my feet, then moved up my legs, my torso, and through my neck and arms. I became weightless. I realized that in order to learn from her, I had to transform and become her. Suddenly, my arms felt like wings and I heard her call out again.

I lifted the instrument to my lips and replied with a trill of descending notes, cascading from the canyon heights to the river below. I called out the melody over and over again until I knew it in my bones. She was my teacher and perhaps I was her teacher as well. I threw in an extra note or two and maybe she thought, "I can do that too."

In this manner, we communicated human to bird, bird to human; breathing together the same air, we drew our breath to sing our song in harmony with each other.

Experiences like the one described above lead me to a sense of freedom in my being, beyond limitations. In the quantum field of all possibilities, we're not limited by our thoughts or what we think we can do or can't do. I was learning the language of God. It wasn't just a communication between human and bird, it was a conversation between God, the Great Spirit, the many multidimensional layers of reality, the creation story, and me.

Element of Water

We move to the south, the element of Water, the ocean, the rain, rivers, and streams. This gentle element represents emotional flow, and the power of the Moon. The energy of water can be used to provide a sense of calm and peacefulness in our lives. When balanced, it can offer a sense of emotional connection and openness, allowing us to flow with our emotions and express ourselves more freely. Combined, water and emotion move energy and information from one place to another. Water flows to the lowest place and entering smoothly, fills any space. Mother Ocean is the birthplace of all living things on Earth. She invites surrender and allowing.

In sound healing, the element of Water can be used to create a sense of relaxation through the use of instruments such as Tibetan and crystal bowls, rainsticks, and ocean drums, which have a gentle and soothing quality. These sounds can release emotional blocks and help us to find a sense of flow and ease in our lives. Water has the power of beauty, to inspire growth and compassion. It's a gentle and flowing force, representing fluidity and connection to the Divine Feminine.

Tuning into the Element of Water

As always, our practice is to tune into the pure, natural sound of the element itself. This can be ocean waves or the sound of flowing water in a creek or fountain. Listening to the falling rain can be a very powerful sonic experience. Hear the myriad melodies cascading through your senses. By contrast, the peaceful sound of a lake on a calm day can take us into a completely different soundscape. Water is a sonic shape-shifter.

Sound Healing Principle—Cymatics

The term "cymatics" is derived from the Greek word "kyma," meaning wave. It is the study of wave phenomena, especially of sounds, and their visual representations. Cymatics describes the effect that sound has on matter; the notion that sound has the ability to create form. The term was coined by the Swiss physician Hans Jenny (1904-1972). The basic concept behind cymatics is that when sound waves pass through a substance, such as sand or water, they cause the particles of that substance to vibrate. These vibrations create specific patterns depending on the frequency and volume of the source sound.

Proponents of holistic medicine believe that the study of

cymatics can be used for healing purposes. They suggest that sound vibrations have the potential to influence the human mind and body in a positive way. Since the body is an electromagnetic energy field, certain frequencies of sound can help to harmonize these elements, leading to health benefits.

Practicing cymatic therapists direct healing frequencies into the body to restore resonance and harmony. The healing frequencies are related to those emitted by a healthy organ or body part. In this way, cymatic healers say, the immune system and other natural regulatory functions are stimulated.

Science tells us that sound waves travel through water faster than through air. Because our bodies are mostly water, we perceive these vibrations at a very deep level. As sound healing practitioners, aware of the cymatics principle, we can use the vibrations we create as a healing balm to relax and align our being at a cellular level. When we relax we feel better.

History of the Tibetan Bowl, Crystal Bowl and Ocean Drum

Tibetan Bowl: Ancient Sound Medicine

Hammered metal bowls, which we know today as singing bowls or Tibetan singing bowls, date back to Persia over 5,000 years ago. The oldest known singing bowl still around today is from Japan and is said to be 1,200 years old. Bowls and bells were made from bronze and various other metals throughout Asia.

The Tibetan bowl actually falls into the category of a resting or horizontal gong. The same process of heating and cooling the metal is used for making suspended gongs. The diameter of the bowl, as well as the thickness of the metal, changes the pitch of the bowl.

One of the magical features of the Tibetan Bowl is the way the pitch can change depending on the environmental conditions of the moment.

Depictions of Buddha, yogis, and other historical figures meditating with and holding singing bowls date back centuries. These early records portray the spiritual and cultural implications of the ritual use of Tibetan singing bowls. Over time, Tibetan bowls have become synonymous with meditation, relaxation, and sound healing practices. The resonant tones produced by striking or rubbing the bowls induce deep relaxation, balance energy, and facilitate spiritual connection.

Crystal Bowl: Angelic Presence

Crystal bowls, a more recent and beloved addition to sound healing journeys, entered the healing music scene in the 1980s. In a beautiful and miraculous occurrence, crystal bowls were birthed from the tech industry. Crystal bowls were created to grow pure silicon, computer chips. If a bowl was not precise enough for growing the chips, they were discarded. At some point along the way, someone discovered that when the bowls were struck, a beautiful, resonant tone was created.

Crystal bowls have found their place in contemporary sound healing practices, meditation sessions, and spiritual rituals. These bowls are typically made of quartz crystal or other gemstones and are carefully crafted and tuned to emit specific frequencies and harmonics. The beautiful tones created by crystal bowls cleanse and balance the body's energy centers, promoting physical, emotional, and spiritual well-being.

While there is no direct evidence of ancient cultures using crystal bowls, some people speculate on this possibility, particularly for cultures that were thriving before recorded history. As many cultures had incredibly advanced technology for their time, it is possible that some included crystal bowls in their sound healing modalities.

Ocean Drum: Serenity of the Sea

A variety of Native groups have an instrument called "the water drum." It is a frame with a deer hide stretched taught and has water inside. These drums are used in ceremonies and dances.

This instrument inspired the creation of another drum. Originally called a geophone, the ocean drum was invented by French composer Olivier Messiaen in 1972. He wanted to recreate the sounds of dry dirt shifting over itself. He built a standard drum frame, but instead of water, put metal beads inside that rolled over the drum head. This produced a whooshing sound that he included in several of his compositions. As time went on, people who heard his music noticed how the geophone emulated the sounds of water rolling over the shore; this is how the name became ocean drum.

These drums are used today in Buddhist meditation and sound healing to inspire long breaths, surrender, and tranquility. The rhythmic sounds of the ocean drum evoke a connection to the natural world, encouraging individuals to find solace and serenity in the gentle rolling waves.

Technique

Bowls

With the Tibetan Bowl or the Crystal Bowl, we want to gently invite the sound from the instrument. We get different tones from the bowl using different types of mallets. A softer mallet will create a softer tone. I think it's best to have some kind of leather covering the wooden mallets so it softens the sound and gives a better contact with the instrument. By spinning the edge of the bowl, we create a consistent, peaceful drone tone, dropping us into a relaxed state.

We can gently strike the sides, drawing the tone out from within the instrument. It might have its own vibrato built in and create an entrainment like pulse. Playing two bowls tuned slightly different from each other creates the binaural beat, which awakens different brainwave states depending on the frequency. Using different bowls in combinations, we can create harmonious chords that evoke a sense of stillness within the flow. [See Appendix D for Brain Wave States]

The bowl is a wonderful instrument to use for entering and exiting the portals, opening and closing the gates into the different dimensions through which we travel during the journey.

You might also want to experiment with putting some water in the bowl to see how sound waves work, just like ripples in a lake when a pebble is dropped in.

Ocean Drum

Take your ocean drum to the beach and listen to your teacher, the sea. Imitate the sound, the constant ebb and flow of the waves. BE the ocean. With a gentle rocking back and forth and around, you can feel the wave sound arising from your instrument. It's a very slow, gentle and smooth technique. When you are playing during the ceremony, imagine the sound of the waves in your mind. Allow it to come forth naturally as you relax into the flow of oceanic expression. Remember to relax your neck and shoulders.

The Golden Ocarina from Ukraine

In 2004, I traveled to the Ukraine to be part of a music team at a spiritual conference. I met a potter there, who was only fifteen years old. He insisted I try to throw the clay to make a pot, but no matter how hard I tried, I could not get it straight! He laughed and I laughed. After the conference was over, we stayed in touch until I returned six years later.

Imagine my surprise when he greeted me with a gift of a golden, clay ocarina. It was beautifully handcrafted. The detail of the design was stunning. Swirls and dots were lovingly carved into the soft golden surface. It was tuned perfectly to a D minor pentatonic scale. The tone is deep and wistful, evoking a sense of timelessness and peace. I do believe that the soul of an instrument has a lot to do with its creator's intentions and blessing. You can hear the love that infuses the clay with every breath that travels through it. He said it was the first one he had ever made, inspired by my flute music. I was speechless. There were no words to express my gratitude and wonder. This sacred instrument is one of my favorite flutes of all time. It accompanies me on every sonic journey.

Invitation to Practice

Find a place near water and play the bowls. Experiment with the different techniques described above. Feel how the presence of water informs your expression. Try different combinations of bowls to see which ones work harmoniously together.

Take the ocean drum to the beach and listen. Practice sounding like the waves, the ebb and flow of the sonic rhythm of the sea. Feel the power of dynamics, a very important principle in music and sound healing.

In stillness
energy moves
In Movement
I am still

Water to Earth

5

Element of Earth

Mother Earth holds us. She breathes, pulses and tones at the low, inaudible, 7.82 cycles per second (cps) during her daily and yearly rotation cycles. We all live in our own rhythms and tones, and are affected by the rhythms and tones of others. All life vibrates with its own harmonic relationship to earth. As we blend languages, peoples, attitudes and religions, we feel new harmonies emerge.

— Don Campbell
The Roar of Silence

Direction: West
Sound Healing Principle: Binaural/Isochronic Beats
Quality: Grounding
Instruments: Drum & Didgeridoo

The Hungarian Wild Red Deerskin Drum

Boom! The sound ran through me like a wild deer in the woods as I took in what was before my eyes. Measuring 30 inches in diameter, the red deerskin drum had an intricate rawhide braiding resembling a dreamcatcher on the backside to hold while playing. I knew this was a drum from my ancestors.

The drum had roots in the forests of Hungary, just as my family does. I could only see a photo of the drum, but I knew it was the one for me. When I held it in my hands and played it for the first time, I was instantly transported. I felt generations of my kin present with me, our hearts beating together in time with the drum, and running wild like the red deer.

Element of Earth

We move to the west, the element of Earth. Earth has the quality of stability and grounding. It represents the physical body. The element of Earth is associated with our sense of safety and security. The energy of Earth can also be used to release anxiety. Earth is represented physiologically in our bodies through minerals like zinc, potassium and magnesium. Experienced on the planet as soil and plants, Sadhguru from India says, "Soil is not a commodity. It is older, wiser, and far more intelligent and capable than you."

Earth is an element most associated with the mountains, forests, and fields. The most stable of all the elements, it is the body of the planet herself. It represents grounding, connection to our physical body and all living beings. We become connected to our collective past through the Earth element; all that has transpired before our birth and will continue after our death. Like a good mother, the Earth element is nurturing, protective, and firm. By working with instruments that have a deep and grounding quality, like the drum and didgeridoo, they can help us to feel grounded and connected to our physical body.

Tuning into the Element of Earth

We all know the pleasure of lying down on a big, green lawn. Spend some time barefoot walking on the Earth and experience the pure, natural presence of the element itself. The earth is a big drum. Listen to cascading rocks, lava flows, earthquakes and any other sound you tune into as you explore your connection to our planet home. Shamanic Drummer Christine Stevens says, "The heartbeat in our body temple is the drum on the altar of our lives. Our bodies become the place to experience the sacred rhythms present in the holiness of life. The drumbeat carries us there".

Sound Healing Principle
Binaural and Isochronic Beats

Frequencies are measured in Hertz, a measurement of cycles per second. Binaural beats are created by simultaneously playing two distinct pitches detuned at the frequency that we wish to create. It creates a wah-wah effect. For example, 100hz and 106hz, two different pitches played together, will create a binaural rhythm of 6 hz and therefore entrain the brain to a theta state of consciousness.

Isochronic beats are like a drumbeat, a single tone, tapping in rhythm at a certain frequency. This creates the same effect on our brain wave state that binaural beats create.

The Difference Between Binaural & Isochronic Beats

The main difference between binaural beats and isochronic tones is that binaural beats are two slightly different tones that are continuous, whereas isochronic tones are single tones that come on and off at regular intervals.

Binaural beats, simply put, are an illusion. What happens when you listen to two pure tones separated into each ear, the tiny difference causes a "frequency mismatch" as the sound travels to the auditory part of your brainstem, says Hector Orozco Perez, an author of a recent study on the mysterious beats. This phenomenon causes the brain wave frequency to entrain to or match the frequency of the resultant rhythm of the two slightly out of tune tones.

Isochronic tones are regular beats of a single tone that are used alongside binaural beats in the process called brainwave entrainment. At its simplest level, an isochronic tone is a tone that is being turned on and off rapidly. They create sharp, distinctive pulses of sound. An example would be a consistent, even tempo drumbeat.

[See Appendix D for full-page Brain Wave States]

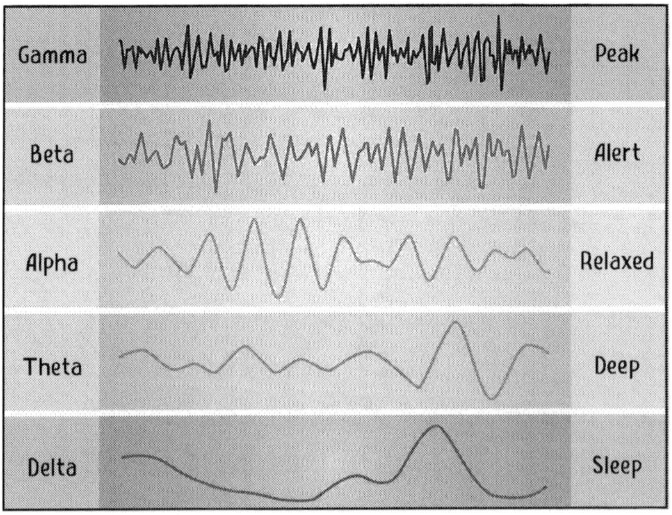

Gamma — Peak
Beta — Alert
Alpha — Relaxed
Theta — Deep
Delta — Sleep

Gamma: insight, peak focus, expanded consciousness.

Beta: alertness, concentration, stress, anxiety, cognition

Alpha: light relaxation, super-learning, visualization, creativity, positive thinking,

Theta: deep relaxation, meditation, increased memory, intuition, focus, dreams, REM sleep

Delta: deep sleep, lucid dreaming, increased immune functions

History of the Drum and Didgeridoo

The Drum: Rhythmic Pulse

In traditional cultures across the globe, musical instruments have served as vital elements of cultural expression, ritualistic ceremonies, and spiritual practices. The drum and didgeridoo are two significant instruments that have played integral roles in diverse traditional societies. Drums have an ubiquitous presence in indigenous tribes worldwide, dating back to our primal ancestors, the Neanderthals, transcending geographical boundaries and cultural diversity. The music of the drum goes back thousands of years, with evidence of its existence found in ancient civilizations such as Egypt, China, Mesopotamia, Africa, and the Americas.

History suggests that both hand drums and drums played with beaters evolved simultaneously. They have played a meaningful role throughout human history and are depicted being used in cultural gatherings and religious ceremonies. They can be made from materials of every type from rocks and gourds, to animal hides, wood and clay.

Culturally, the drum holds immense significance. It serves as a rhythmic pulse that unites communities during social gatherings, celebrations, and religious ceremonies. The drumbeat acts as a unifying force, synchronizing individuals and fostering a sense of collective identity. The cultural context of the drum reflects its role as a symbol of cultural heritage, unity, and connection to ancestral traditions. Drums are also used for communication, signaling important events or emergencies across vast distances.

The Didgeridoo: Deep Resonance

At times, simply called "a didge," the didgeridoo is one of the most ancient instruments originating in the aboriginal lands of present-day Australia. They are traditionally created from the trunk of various trees that are hollowed out by termites while the tree is still living. This instrument was first developed from the groups that lived in the northernmost part of Australia, called Arnhem Land. Two different instruments called the Mago, slightly smaller than the didgeridoo, and Yagaki, a more conical-shaped instrument, comprise the didge's ancestral lineage. The name "didgeridoo" is said to have originated from white settlers when they first encountered these instruments. The sound they heard emanating echoed the sounds of "didgeridoo," hence its common name today.

Didgeridoos have been used in rites, initiations, and rituals throughout aboriginal culture, and this tradition is still carried on today. It is believed to connect individuals with the Dreamtime, the Aboriginal creation period, and ancestral spirits. The didgeridoo's powerful vibrations and rhythmic patterns are utilized for meditation, healing rituals, and spiritual journeying, fostering a deep connection to the land, ancestors, and cultural heritage.

A didgeridoo player would often accompany a singer and a dancer in a variety of ceremonies to help tell the stories, myths, and history of the culture. This oral heritage has ensured that the truth of these groups has survived the test of time and it continues today. Today, the didgeridoo is associated with Aboriginal culture as a whole, and many more groups than just those from Arnhem Land have incorporated this instrument into their sacred practices.

Technique

The Drum

There are many different types of drums and each has a unique voice. The round frame drum is the most popular style for a sound healing practice. The most important thing is to find a drum with a tone that you resonate with. Some people say, "Your drum finds you." Explore with your mallet the different areas of the surface to find the "sweet spot". You can also rub your hand across the surface and create a soft, wind-like sound.

Here are some basic rhythms that we employ for a sound healing ceremony:

Entrainment beat: A steady single note beat at 60 bpm. This is also called an isochronic beat.

Heartbeat: boom, boom, rest…

Dance Beat (known as the Clave beat): **1** and 2 **AND** 3 and **4** and...

Clave is the most popular world-wide rhythm used in every genre of music. In pop music it's sometimes called the "Hand-Jive Beat" Master percussionist Kim Atkinson says, "The use of the word Clave as a contemporary musical term is most connected with Cuba, where Clave is so important in the folkloric and popular music that is could be considered a philosophy or musical approach."

In 4/4 time (4 beats to a measure, 8 half-beats):
strike on beat **1**
the **AND** of 2
and the **4**

Didgeridoo

The Didgeridoo is a fabulous instrument for creating a deep, grounding drone experience. Using circular breathing (breathing in through the nose while simultaneously breathing out through the mouth), a constant tone is created, like holding down a key on an organ. The mouth position, or embouchure, is similar to a trumpet, buzzing the lips. Different sounds can be evoked by singing and toning while playing. Animal sounds and jungle noises are popular themes employed by didge players. The harmonic overtone series is also present as in all drone instruments and these can be brought out and emphasized by a skilled player. I am not a didgeridoo player so cannot expand much on the technique. There are many great players and if you are sincere about learning, you will attract the right teacher.

Crystal Wind

I had scrambled up to a small opening on the side of a rocky mountain above a wilderness lake. I intended to spend the night outdoors at a high elevation to take in the fresh mountain air. Settling in under a ledge, I waited for stars to begin their nightly parade across the midnight sky.

As I drifted into the darkness, wispy clouds began to build into giant thunderheads. I felt the deep, low frequencies of a rising thunderstorm. The sound waves rumbled through my body, it was very close. It was like the grandest gong bath you can imagine. I breathed deeply in the electrified air.

The cracks in the sky were like a whip across eternity, shrieking in ferocious power. It felt like the thunder would crack the rocks like shattering ice. The earth shook me like a friend trying to rouse me the morning after. The wind was whistling an urgent melody as shivers raced through my body. I felt like I was having a holy roller revelation.

I fell asleep as rain pelted the moonscape around me. When I awoke the next day the air was clear as crystal. The morning sky was blue beyond forever. I was healed and the words, Crystal Wind, rang through my awareness. Thus was born the name for my music business. I realized I had just been through a vision quest, crying for guidance in my life. Like Jimmy Buffet says, "The Sound of the Weather is Heaven's Ragtime Band." I was now a part of the celestial orchestra and had found my place in the world.

Invitation to Practice

Take your drum or didgeridoo out on the Earth and tune in to the vibration of the land. Create a sacred circle, a container to hold your experience. Start with a simple beat and keep it going. As always with sound healing, we are invoking a peaceful state of consciousness more than showing off our technique. Allow yourself to go on a sonic voyage. Invite the presence of benevolent energies into your circle. At the end of your practice, allow for some quiet time to integrate the revelations, insights, and visions of your journey. Give thanks to the land for your time together.

Earth to Air

Element of Air

Stress, depression, fatigue and overexcitement can be transformed into an awakened and relaxed state with the use of sound. Within two to three minutes, the mind and body can be brought into a clearer, more balanced state.

— Don Campbell
The Roar of Silence

Direction: North
Sound Healing Principle: Harmonics
Quality: Freedom
Instruments: Flute & Feather

God is in the Overtones

The sound of "OM" resounded through the room in wave after wave. Hundreds of voices were joined in one sound and it felt like the heavens opened up. The illusion that separated "me" from "them" dissolved. We were one body, singing in unison, with the harmony of angels accompanying us.

The harmonic overtones of our voices shivered up my spine, rippling through my body. We were dancing our voices together and co-creating the overtones of life itself. My heart was blown wide open revealing a soft, warm center, connecting me to the All. I not only heard the overtones, I had a full body somatic experience of a musical principle. This revelation expanded and I knew that all of Creation is frequency and vibration.

Element of Air

Moving to the final element, we come back to the breath, to the element of Air in the north. Air is the element of movement and has the quality of freedom. It represents the power of the wind and the breath of life. This element is often associated with the sky and clouds. The breath of life, the breath in our lungs, both guiding and reflecting our experience on Earth. Air is unstable, ungrounded, light, swift, and etheric. It allows us to have a higher perspective. It is through air that we are able to connect to the upper realms of the shamanic world. Change arrives with the wind. Depending on the direction the wind is coming from, blessings or challenges were predicted across cultures. When balanced, it can provide a sense of feeling more connected to the world around us.

Air is also the element of communication, new perspective, and the mind. It can act as a bridge between the earth and fire element, as it connects physically with the burning of material. A fire can only burn so long as it has access to some air. Air is part of the transformation process that takes place within. The ego, the mind, must be burned away and be released in order to allow the new to unfold. The air allows the process of burning to take place. Wind currents direct where the flow of water goes. Air stores and categorizes information, as the mind does.

In sound healing, the element of Air can be used to create a sense of openness and expansion through the use of instruments such as flutes, feathers and chimes, which have a light and airy quality.

Tuning Into the Element of Air

Here again we tune into the pure, natural sound of the element itself. The sound of wind in the trees, the rhythm of your own breath, the flapping of wings as a murmuration of birds soars overhead. Wind is the breath of Earth, ever-changing and sometimes absent in the stillness of the doldrums. Even when calm, our breath continues, unabated, perennial as time itself. The Bible says, "Be still and know". Take some time to BE with the Air element, it is Life itself.

Sound Healing Principle: Harmonics / Overtones

A harmonic, or overtone, is a wave with a frequency that is a positive integer multiple of a fundamental frequency. Pythagoras, in ancient Greece, is said to have discovered the harmonic ratios in sound. The fundamental tone is called the 1st harmonic. The other harmonics are vibrating at 2 times, 3 times, etc., of that fundamental frequency and form the harmonic series. The term is employed in various disciplines, including music and sound healing. These harmonic notes are subtly present in every natural instrument that's played. In my experience, when an instrument is played using the natural harmonic overtone series, our bodies perceive it as comforting, as these frequency relationships are present in all of nature.

The most powerful interval is the 3rd harmonic, or the 5th. Playing two notes together with this interval creates a sonic environment that is both soothing and relaxing. You can use a Keyboard or a Shruti box to achieve this effect.

On stringed instruments, harmonics are played by lightly

touching, but not fully pressing down, the string at an exact point while sounding the string. This allows the harmonic to sound, a pitch which is always higher than the fundamental frequency of the string. The combination of overtones present in an instrument's sound creates the particular tone color or timbre of that instrument.

[See Appendix C for full-page Harmonic Overtone Series]

Partial	Note	Interval
1	C	Unison
2	C	Octave
3	G	Perfect 5th
4	C	Octave
5	E	Major 3rd
6	G	Perfect 5th
7	B^b	Minor 7th
8	C	Octave
9	D	Major 2nd
10	E	Major 3rd
11	F#	Augmented 4th
12	G	Perfect 5th
13	A^b	Minor 6th
14	B^b	Minor 7th
15	B	Major 7th
16	C	Octave

Harmonics may also be called partials. The difference between harmonic and overtone is that the former includes all of the notes in a series, including the fundamental frequency, while the latter only includes the pitches above the fundamental. Some musical contexts use the terms harmonics, overtones and partials interchangeably.

As a living example of the phenomenon of overtones, you may have heard of the Tuvan throat singers. Throat singing is a captivating vocal technique originating from Tuva, Russia, where singers manipulate their vocal tract to produce multiple harmonically rich pitches simultaneously, emphasizing specific overtones of a fundamental note. Thus a unique timbre or tone quality of each voice is created, depending on the blend of partials. This technique is deeply connected to the harmonic overtone series in music, allowing singers to create mesmerizing melodies of harmonics above a drone-like fundamental pitch. Tuvan throat singing encompasses various styles such as sygyt with its flute-like tones, kargyraa with its deep guttural sound, and khoomei combining high and low overtones, all rooted in Tuvan cultural traditions and reflecting a profound relationship with nature.

History of the Flute and Feather

The Flute: Breath of Life

The oldest known musical instrument is a flute from a cave in present-day Slovenia called Divje Babe. This flute is made from the femur bone of a cave bear and features precisely-spaced holes that look to have been drilled. Other Paleolithic flutes have been found across the globe as well. Ancient flutes have been found in regions as diverse as China, Egypt, Greece, India, and the Americas, suggesting that the flute was independently developed in different parts of the world.

Made from vulture bones, swan bones, and mammoth ivory, flutes have been in humans' musical repertoire since long before recorded history. The use of flutes are also depicted in ancient Egyptian art and were found perfectly preserved in several tombs. Panpipes have been depicted in ancient Egyptian culture as well as South American culture. In Southeast Asia, panpipes are bound together in a circle. Pan pipes also have a well respected place in

European classical music.

The flute holds profound cultural significance across various traditional societies. In many cultures, the flute is associated with spirituality, mysticism, and the power to communicate with the Divine. The breath required to play the flute mirrors the breath of life and the music produced is seen as a dialogue with the elements and the Spirit World. The ability of the flute to mimic the sounds of nature, such as birdsong and flowing water, gracefully represents the element of air in a sound healing experience.

Traditional flutes exhibit a rich diversity of forms, playing techniques, and cultural practices. For instance, the Native American flute, with its distinctive sound and construction, is deeply intertwined with the spirituality and cultural heritage of indigenous peoples of North America. In other parts of the world, instruments like the Bansuri in India, the Xiao in China, and the Ney in the Middle East have their own unique cultural significance and musical traditions. While the flute has evolved over time and embraced modern adaptations, its traditional essence continues to resonate in contemporary contexts.

The Feather: Soothing Grace

In researching the history of the feather, the most common use is as an adornment. In my own personal experience, I learned about how to use the feather as a sound healing tool from Tito. From the stories I have been told, it originated as an instrument to use in sacred ceremonies and for healing by Shamans. Finding a feather in the forest is an auspicious gift from the elements and Nature herself. Honoring the source of our instrumental allies is an important part of our sound healing practice. Using feathers can evoke a genuine lightness of being for both the practitioner and the listener.

Technique

The Flute

The flute, the place of air in the north. We come back to the breath, to the place where we began our journey. The place of the silent Om. We awaken the flute with our breath. We practice long, easy tones with a relaxed neck, supporting the breath, just like we do with the voice. The flute becomes an extension of our voice. We are singing through the flute.

With our breath, we blow across the holes, awakening the instrument. Inviting the sound from the flute, we allow it to teach us, inform us what it wants to say. Playing each note, one by one, starting with long tones, all the notes open, just free flowing air through the hollow chamber. Descending down, we close one hole, one note at a time, maybe bring in a little vibrato, which is creating waves with our breath, like the wah-wah of the binaural beat.

When playing a transverse flute like the classical silver flute or the Indian bamboo Bansuri flute, blow across the opening like blowing across a glass bottle top. Purse the lips and keep the air opening as small as possible and work on keeping a steady, even tone. Roll the flute in or out to tune as necessary.

If you are playing a Native American flute or a South American Quena flute, there are five notes, the pentatonic scale. We keep listening to the tone of it, listening to what it wants to say. From this place, we allow the simple healing melodies to come forth. From a prayerful place, we resonate with the vibrations of the flute, bringing ourselves into alignment.

The Feather

One of my favorite instruments, the feather, has a profound effect on people during a sonic ceremony. It creates a sense of well-being, like a healing wind. It might sound like a bird flying through the room, evoking a sense of possibility and freedom.

We start by swishing the feather loud and gradually get softer, like a delay created in a canyon. Like a train as it passes through the landscape. We are creating a soundscape oasis, a place of rest and healing. The feather can be lightly touched on a person in a gentle, playful way, or fluttered around the body with an intention of purification. It is simple yet profound. Experiment with different sonic possibilities as the feather teaches you.

Grandfather Flute

I could hear his footsteps crunching the dry grass as he approached me from across the field, carrying a 5 foot long staff of bamboo. I had not seen my friend Kim, from college African drum class, for some time. "I think this flute has your name on it," he offered.

We were both arriving for a sound healing session with our mutual teacher, Tito La Rosa, whose son, Omar, had fashioned this beautiful instrument. Kim had acquired the Abuelo, Grandfather Flute, some years back, and was not using it anymore. Something inside him said it was now to go to Bodhi. At that time in my life, I had not heard of such an instrument, and was delighted to learn about it, and glad to add it to my orchestra. It has since become one of my most trusted allies in this work. It expresses the natural harmonic overtone series with such clarity and beauty. It always enchants the participants on the journey.

When you commit to the path of music and sound healing, the perfect instruments will manifest in the most magical ways.

Grandfather Abuelo Flute

Invitation to Practice

Listen to the wind as the breath of earth. Listen to the sound of your breath as the wind of your body. Feel the life force energy flowing through your body, your body is a flute. Play your flute. Play with the feather. Feel your breath deepening as you allow these sacred instruments to teach you and awaken your inner sound healer.

Inkwash cloud etchings
  please me again
    painting the day
as they change
  slowly
    more explicit than words

7

Harmonizing The Elements

All that the beasts and the green things do, is well done, and rightly done. All of these act within the equilibrium. From the hurricane and the great whales' sounding, to the fall of a dry leaf and the gnat's flight, all they do is done within the balance of the whole. But we, insofar as we have power over the world and over one another, we must learn to do what the leaf and the whale and the wind do of their own nature. We must learn to keep the balance. Having intelligence, we must not act in ignorance. Having choice, we must not act without responsibility.

— Ursula K Le Guin

Putting it All Together

In this chapter we talk about:

- Performance Flow Charts
- Transitions
- Attracting Your Perfect Instruments
- Instrument Mesa
- Collaborating with Other Sound Healers
- Harmonious Connections Between Instruments
- Medicine Hat
- Creating a Sound Healing Experience

Keep Going

"Keep going," was all he said. My painting teacher is a Japanese Zen master named Kazuaki Tanahashi, people simply call him Kaz. He taught me how to paint the Enso, the sacred Japanese circle, drawn in a single stroke.

Eventually, I had my own art show and Kaz was going to attend. I scheduled a personal showing with him so he could see my work up close and assess my progress. As he approached, my hands began to sweat. He looked at every painting thoughtfully, but didn't say a word. I considered his body language. I read into every twitch of his eye, every torque of his mouth. Although I had told myself to be calm, I couldn't help but wonder if my work was good enough for him.

After inspecting every piece, he donned his coat and prepared to leave. He hadn't said a word yet. I was beside myself with anticipation. The thoughts of doubt began to creep in like a dark cloud hiding the sun.

His foot was almost over the threshold of the door before he turned around. He uttered the two words that would inspire me for years to come, "Keep going." At first, I was taken aback. There was no praise, no "Good job." I felt deflated. Then, the light of clarity shone and I got chills. Like the Enso, his words revealed the power of simplicity. Like the Enso, I would circle around and begin again.

In this chapter, we explore how to harmonize the elements in sound healing to create a balanced and transformative experience.

We look at different sound healing techniques and how to combine them to create a powerful and effective sonic journey. Harmonizing the elements is about creating a balance between the different energies represented by each element. We might use them in a specific sequence or order that reflects their natural, energetic flow.

For example, we can start with the element of Ether to create a sense of spaciousness and clarity, then move to the element of Fire to promote transformation and release, followed by Water to promote emotional healing and relaxation, then Earth to promote grounding and stability, and finally Air to promote openness and expansion. The key to harmonizing the elements is to be intuitive and creative, experimenting with different combinations and sequences to find what works best for each unique sound healing journey. By blending the different elements, we can create a harmonious and holistic experience that promotes healing and balance in the body, mind, and spirit.

In my lineage of sound healing with Peruvian teacher, Tito La Rosa, I was taught to use sacred cleansing tools such as Sage, Agua de Florida and Palo Santo, among others, during sound healing ceremonies. I understand that there are conflicting views on the use of indigenous traditions by those born outside of those traditions and as a student of Tito, I want to carry on the tradition of sound healing as he taught it to me. In my practice as a sound healing practitioner, I embrace the wisdom of many different cultures around the world.

To create a Sonic Ceremony, there are several techniques to consider. These include setting an intention for the ceremony, gentle invocation of the natural elements and sounds, creating portals or entry points into the ceremony, transitions between different sounds and instruments, stillness and silence to allow for integration, and being sensitive to individual and group needs.

We want to consider which harmonious combinations of instruments we choose to create each portal. Using drones as a foundation, we can access different moods with different music modes. With the shruti box, monochord, keyboard, or the didgeridoo, we create a sonic field with a bass note, or home tone for the other instruments to harmonize and blend with. Within that portal is the freedom to express what's needed in the moment from whatever instrument is required. The combination of the elements, the acoustic instruments and the natural sounds of animals, insects, wind, and water is the basis of the soundtrack.

There's so much intuition that goes into creating a sonic ceremony that one might also include a study of how to listen and feel deeply. The deeper we listen, and surrender into sacred space, the more we can access guidance and powers not normally available to us. There's such a plethora of possibilities in every moment. Our mission and purpose is to pay attention to the tiny impulses as well as grand revelations. Thus we become an antenna for creativity and healing. We awaken the portal, or the container where each individual can relax into their perfect alignment. Sound Practitioner and Gong Master, Guy Douglas says, "The less it's about me, the more potent the experience."

To summarize, creating a sound healing journey involves intentional use of instruments and a focus on harmonious connections between them, while utilizing techniques such as intention, gentle invocation, portals, transitions, stillness/silence, and sensitivity to individual and group needs.

One to One vs Group Experiences

Although the instruments and sound techniques are the same for a group as they are for an individual, the way we approach the session is a bit different. I think we need to be more sensitive to volume as we work one on one. There needs to be a delicate sensitivity to the close proximity factor. Also, we can tune directly into the unique energy of one person as opposed to a large group. In a group, there is a broader sense of the overall energy in the room. As you work over time, you will discern more subtle differences between these experiences.

Performance Flow Charts

When you are first beginning, it's good to have a set list or flow chart of portals to journey through. As you progress over time, adding new instruments and expanding your technique, new portals will emerge and some will be birthed spontaneously as you deepen into knowing what each ally is capable of. It's also good to include the key and mode when relevant. As we memorize these, we start to intuitively know which instruments are compatible together.

A sample sound healing sequence might look like this:

Opening invocation: Tibetan Bowl or Crystal Bowl

Portal of opening: D-Drone with simple Flute or Vocalization pattern in a pentatonic scale

Portal of Clearing: gentle Rattle rhythm for a few minutes.

Portal of Emptiness: The Gong

Portal of Power: steady drumbeat

Portal of Freedom: Am-Native Flute with Drone background

Portal of Relaxation: Ocean Drum or Crystal Bowl

Portal of Completion: Feather and/or Chimes to gently bring people back into their bodies

For different occasions, we can invoke the portals of the heart, the feminine or masculine, portals of intuition and many other creative elements of healing that begin to open up as we continue our practice. Whether working one-on-one or in a group, it is essential to respect personal space and the unique needs of each individual present. Remember our guiding principle from Jonathan Goldman, "Frequency plus Intention equals Healing."

Transitions

Transitions play a very important role in the course of the sound journey. Slow and gradual, graceful and smooth, moving from one portal to another, like the tides or the flowing of a river into a bay out to the sea. Some basic ideas for transitions are:

- Silence, with a slow fade out and slow fade in
- Bell or Bowl
- Drone note change, with a slow fade out and slow fade in
- Connecting tones: match notes of previous mode to new mode
- Rattle and Leaf Shaker
- The Feather
- Breath Sounds

Completing the Journey

Bringing your listeners out of the journey is a very important completion step. It's always good to have a few minutes of silence at the end. Then with a soft, gentle voice, invite people to come back to the awareness of their breath. After a few breaths, you want to invite them to come back into an awareness of their body by wiggling their fingers and their toes, gently rolling their neck and stretching their spine. When it is comfortable, ask them to lay on their side and rest here for a while before coming to a seated position. You might want to end by chanting three "Oms" together. If it's a small enough group, a period of sharing their experience can be fruitful for helping people remember what they experienced, or learned on the journey.

Attracting Your Perfect Instruments: Letting Them Find You

The ten instruments shared in this book are common in the sound healing world. Any combination of them along with your own collection would be a perfect core to begin or expand your orchestra. Play around with where each of your instruments fit, for you, in the combination of elements. What qualities emanate from its tone palette? Where does it feel at home?

When you envision the instruments for your orchestra, pay attention to the feeling you have inside as you picture them. Allow them to manifest in your life. Over time, the perfect sonic constellation will gather around you, they will find you. They will guide you in your practice if you allow them. The sounds of wisdom that reside within each instrument are the real teachers. Much of learning about sound healing is discovering what's already there.

Here is a partial list of the allies in my Orchestra:

- **12 String Guitar**
- **Charango**
- **Conch Shell**
- **Crystal Xylophone**

- **Drum**
- **Echo Harmonica**
- **Electronic Keyboard**
- **Feather wand**
- **Flutes from around the world**
- **Gong**
- **Koshi chimes**
- **Nylon string guitar**
- **Ocarina**
- **Ocean drum**
- **Rattles, Shakers and Leaf Shakers (Chakapa)**
- **Shruti Box**
- **Singing Frame Drum**
- **Tibetan Bowl**
- **Ukulele**

Other popular sound healing instruments:

- **Didgeridoo**
- **Handpan**
- **Harp**
- **Monochord**
- **Tuning Forks**
- **Vibraphone**
- **Violin**

Instrument Mesa

In the sound healing school of Tito La Rosa, creating a "Mesa" for our instruments is part of the tradition. It means "table" in Spanish and it acts like an altar to hold our "allies," which is how we call the instruments and their part in the ceremony. One day, I found a beautiful, handmade, one of a kind blanket from Peru, named Purple Rain. I knew immediately that it was to be my Mesa. Your Mesa will come when you call it in on your journey as a sound healing practitioner.

Acoustic and Electric

Acoustic medicine with the intention of healing has been around as long as humans could sing and express themselves musically. Playing instruments without amplification is the most natural way to experience Sound Healing. I personally enjoy the pure acoustic sessions very much. However, there is a time and a place, especially with very large groups, that using a PA system is necessary for broadcasting the sound over a large area.

Playing natural instruments through a microphone is the next level of performance beyond pure acoustic. In this scenario, the natural sound is preserved even though it is amplified. When we start using electric instruments that are designed to be played with amplification, we've taken it to another level. I love this experience, especially when using a "looper," which can capture and record phrases that are repeated over and over, layering it with other sounds that harmoniously blend in. I am able to create a sonic world that is very deep and wide, allowing the participants to travel through a plethora of amazing portals.

This practice involves another learning curve to understand how sound reinforcement works using mixers and microphones, etc. Some people argue that the benefits are not as pure coming through speakers. I believe that sound and intention together creates a positive experience. With this philosophy, we can manifest a healing environment in any and all contexts.

Collaborating with Other Sound Healing Practitioners

Creating sound healing journeys with other musicians is one of my favorite explorations. At some point, once you feel comfortable in your own practice, you will probably feel called to expand into playing with one or two other people. The largest ensemble I've directed was 6 sound healers. It was a lot of preparation and rehearsal and the experience was powerful for all the players and the audience. We went into some amazing, magical spaces.

Here are some tips for successful collaborations:

- Know your instruments and what key they are in. i.e. what notes and modes do you to offer to the collective creation.
- Cross reference your notes with the other players to find potential starting places for opening a portal.
- Each participant creates at least one portal unless you are spontaneously and magically connecting in the quantum field as one heart and one mind.
- Listen first, wait a little bit longer before you enter the conversation with a sound.
- Be conscious of the "set and setting," the kind of environment you co-create.
- Allow space for learning something new from each other.
- Be clear about what tuning system you are using: 440, 432, etc.

Soundscape Oasis Sound Healing Orchestra 2019
L to R: Cypress Dubin, Barbara Juniper, Bodhi Starwater, Gabriel Harris, René Jenkins, Janet Janay Cipriani

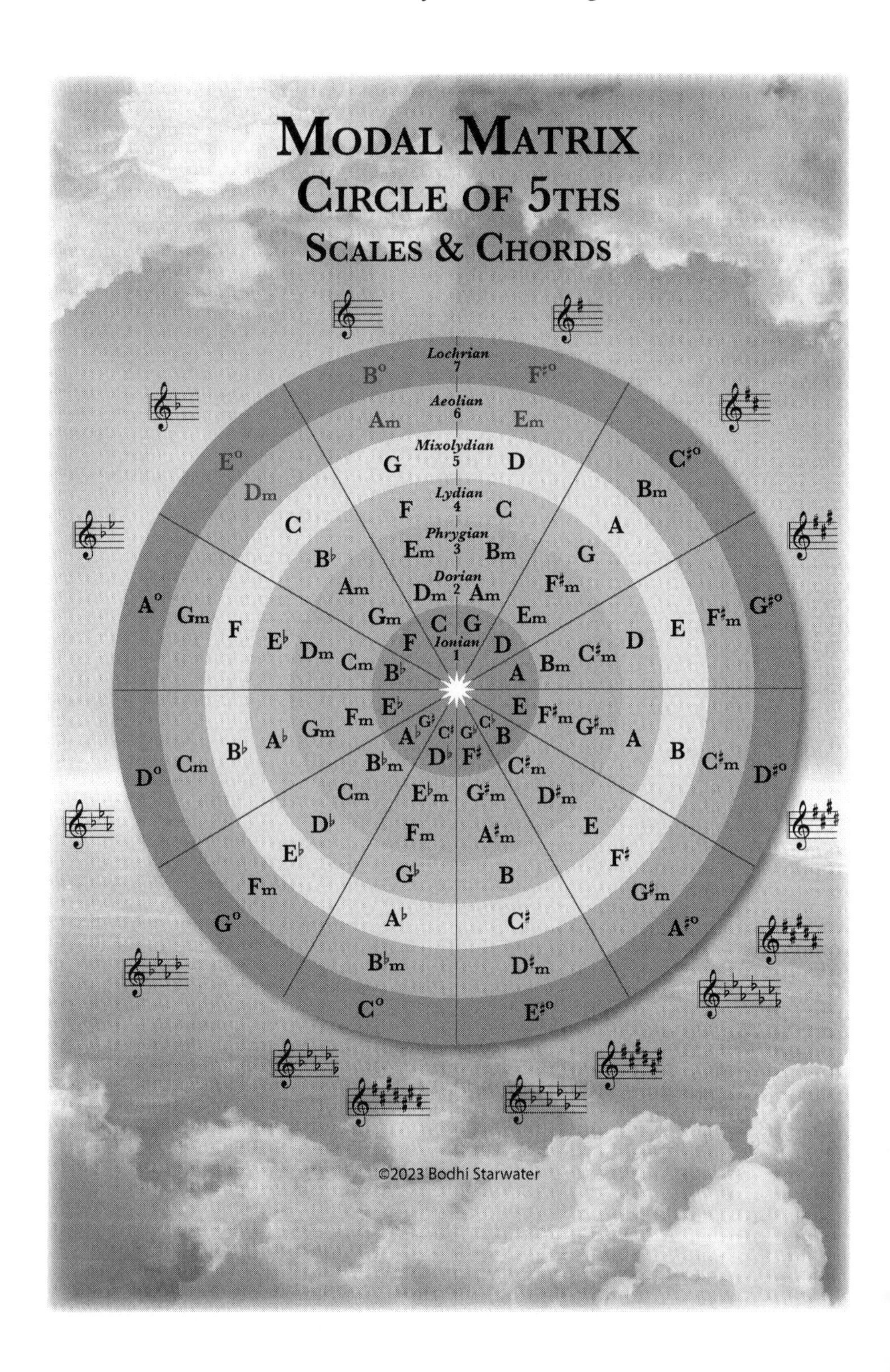
Modal Matrix
Circle of 5ths
Scales & Chords
Lochrian 7
B° F♯° C♯° G♯° D♯° A♯° E♯° C° G° D° A° E°
Aeolian 6
Am Em Bm F♯m C♯m G♯m D♯m B♭m Fm Cm Gm Dm
Mixolydian 5
G D A E B F♯ C♯ A♭ E♭ B♭ F C
Lydian 4
F C G D A E B G♭ D♭ A♭ E♭ B♭
Phrygian 3
Em Bm F♯m C♯m G♯m D♯m A♯m Fm Cm Gm Dm Am
Dorian 2
Dm Am Em Bm F♯m C♯m G♯m E♭m B♭m Fm Cm Gm
Ionian 1
C G D A E B C♭ F♯ G♭ D♭ C♯ A♭ G♯ E♭ B♭ F
©2023 Bodhi Starwater

Music Theory

The purpose of the Modal Matrix Chart is to learn enough about music theory so you can match instruments based on the notes each can play. One basic principle of music is the concept of intervals, which is the distance between two notes. Think of it like a ruler with 12 inches. The distance of one inch is the same no matter where it is placed. The same is true for the relationship between the 12 notes of Western music.

Built into this chart is a very common music teaching tool called the circle of 5ths. In the clockwise direction, we have the interval of a 5th. Going counter clockwise, we have the interval of a 4th. Going from the center out, we have the notes of the major scale and the chords that naturally fall within those scales.

To begin with, focus on just one slice of the pie. We'll start with the note C in the center left. If you are looking at a piano, C is the note just below the group of 2 black keys. This pattern of 2-3 black keys repeats over the entire keyboard. The movement from one key to the adjacent white or black key is called a half step. Two half steps equal one whole step.

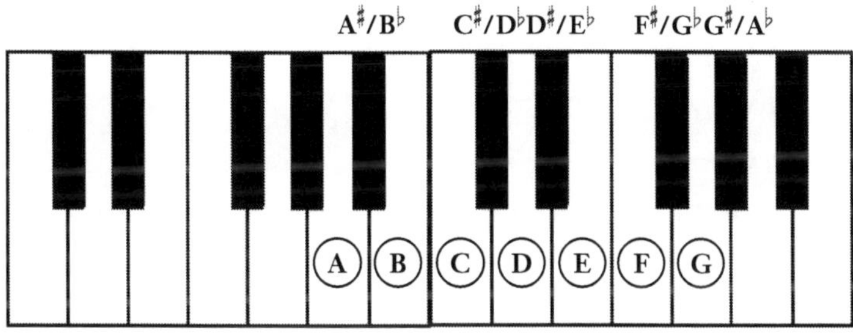

For the names of the white piano keys, we use the first 7 letters of the alphabet: A, B, C, D, E, F, G. The black keys are named for an adjacent white key with a sharp (#) if the black key is to the right of the white key (which raises the pitch a half step), or a flat (b) if the black key is to the left of the white key (which lowers the pitch a half step).

There are many different musical scales throughout the cultures of the world. For our purposes, we're using the seven note major scale, 1–7, as a common starting place. The pattern for a major scale is always the same, no matter what key you begin with. Start with the "1", the fundamental, the tonic, or home tone, then continue: whole step, whole step, half step, whole step, whole step, whole step and half step to reach the octave, the home tone again.

1 2 3 4 5 6 7 1 (Octave)
W W H W W W H
Do Re Mi Fa Sol La Ti Do

Using "1" as the home tone, the intervals build from this point. Moving from one note to another is what we call an interval (the distance between 2 notes). Therefore this scale has intervals of a 2nd, 3rd, 4th, 5th, 6th and 7th from the home tone. The interval of a 5th is one of the basic musical elements of sound healing. The other intervals most useful in a Sound Healing practice are the minor 3rd, the major 3rd, the 4th and 6th.

One can create different modes or moods by starting on a different note within the major scale. With **C** as our home tone, using only the white notes of the keyboard, we have the IONIAN or MAJOR scale. The interval of a 5th in this mode will be C to G. This mode is generally associated with a happy or playful mood.

You can choose **D** as your home tone and use only the white keys (the same notes as the C major scale), and you will create the mode of D Dorian (D, E, F, G, A, B, C, D). The interval of a 5th in this mode will be D to A. This mode can evoke a Celtic music feeling.

If you make **E** your home tone, and use only the white keys, you will have the Phrygian mode (E, F, G, A, B, C, D, E). The interval of a 5th in this mode will be E to B. This mode evokes more of a Middle Eastern feeling.

If you make **F** your home tone, and use only the white keys, you will have the Lydian mode (F, G, A, B, C, D, E, F). The interval of a 5th in this mode will be the notes F to C. This mode evokes an open and majestic, bright sunny feeling.

If you make **G** your home tone, and use only the white keys, you will have the Mixolydian mode (G, A, B, C, D, E, F, G). The interval of a 5th in this mode will be the notes G to D. This mode best expresses the natural overtone series and is the basic scale and feeling of blues music.

If you make **A** your home tone, and use only the white keys, you will have the Aeolian or Minor mode (A, B, C, D, E, F, G, A). The interval of a 5th in this mode will be the notes A to E. This mode is traditionally associated with a melancholy or somber mood.

If you make **B** your home tone and use only the white keys, you will have the Locrian mode (B, C, D, E, F, G, A, B). The interval of a 5th in this mode will be the notes B to F. However, it is a diminished 5th - one half step smaller than any of the other fifths - and for this reason, this mode is rarely used in anything except avant-garde music where more dissonant and obscure sounds like the diminished 5th are the norm.

If you have an instrument that's in a C major scale, the same notes as all the white keys on a piano, and you want to play with a didgeridoo in the note of D, you can play your instrument in a D Dorian mode by matching the D home tone of the didge. If you study the chart, you can reference any set of notes that your instrument has and figure out where it fits in the modal matrix. Knowing what key and mode you are playing in is a basic skill you can develop over time. This is a very useful when collaborating with other sound healers.

You can see that in each of these modes, except Locrian, we have an interval of a perfect fifth as the structure around which we build our sound healing melodies. A couple of tips for creating musical phrases in the context of sound healing are:

- Play long tones
- Open the phrase with the interval of a 5th.
- Play melodies slow and simple.
- Repeat phrases—repetition is a form of entrainment
- Use space and silence.

Another fascinating facet of music theory is the pentatonic scale, or 5 note scale. These 5 notes are universal around the globe in Native cultures. There are many variations of the 5 note patterns in the different tuning systems of the world. In Western music, using just the white notes of the piano, the pentatonic scale is:

C D E G A C
W W W+H W W+H
Do Re Mi Sol La Do

An example from a different key **D** would be:

D	**E**	**F#**	**A**	**B**	**D**
W	**W**	**W+H**	**W**	**W+H**	
Do	**Re**	**Mi**	**Sol**	**La**	**Do**

Extensively used in folk and rock music, many famous melodies, such as "Amazing Grace," use these 5 notes exclusively. A simple way to hear what this scale sounds like is to play all the black notes on a piano which are laid out naturally as a pentatonic scale. This example is the F# pentatonic scale (F#, G#, A#, C#, D#). Learning the pentatonic scale from any pitch is useful for creating a varied and melodious sound healing experience.

All of these principles that we have discussed here are in the Key of C. You can use this chart (the Modal Matrix) to apply to all 12 keys (white and black notes) and match your instruments depending on what notes they have. [See Appendix E for Modal Matrix]

Medicine Hat

Another sacred element of the ceremony is my Medicine Hat. It helps to put me in the proper state of focus and concentrated intention. It was quite magical how this hat came to me. I was invited to participate in a store blessing ceremony that included a new line of medicine hats that the store would carry. I was fortunate enough to be the first ever to buy a hat from the shop. After I purchased the hat and the ceremony was closed, I went to visit the hatmaker and we adorned it with amethyst crystals, silver charms, and the figure of a deity who is known as the cosmic flute player, Kokopelli. I wear this hat only during my sonic ceremonies.

Invitation: Create a Sound Healing Journey

Now is the time when things begin to get interesting. We've all heard the word "practice" all of our lives. What does it mean to you now in your life? It seems to be an axiom that in order to master something we must do it many times. I must have heard the number 10,000, 10,000 times. So we practice our instruments and we practice the principles.

Invite some friends over, set the space, create the container and share what you have learned. Be conscious of the "set and setting." Set and setting are factors that can condition the effects of ones' experience: "Set" refers to the mental state a person brings to the experience, like thoughts, mood and expectations; "setting" to the physical and social environment.

With a few words of introduction, invite your audience to breathe gently, relax and let go into the experience. With each journey you will learn more and deepen your practice and skill.

Conclusion

The written word is merely a symbol to be reproduced and only expresses its full value by its restoration to sound. Writing only carries meaning when the reader hears the sounds in front of him.

— Alfred A. Tomatis

Everything is energy and that's all there is to it. Match the frequency of the reality you want and you cannot help but get that reality. It can be no other way. This is not philosophy. This is physics.

— Albert Einstein

Paul Horn

It was the phenomenal resonance of Paul Horn's flute in the Taj Mahal that set me on the path to playing the flute when I was fourteen. Through his musical recordings, I found an inspirational teacher, a mentor, and later, a friend. As an adult, I had the great opportunity to study with him. He passed on many secrets and techniques about the flute that I employ and teach to this day.

After recording my *Shamanic Flute* album, I sent him a copy. His response was written on a card with a gold flute embossed on the front. Along with his thanks, all he had written was, "Keep the music going."

Horn's beautiful Taj Mahal album, *Inside* (1969), was the catalyst for me to begin playing the flute, but this letter reawakened the enthusiasm of a beginner's mind. I had already begun the journey and he told me to keep going, just like Kaz, my Zen painting teacher. Maybe that's what all masters say to their students, "Keep going."

The more we keep going, the more we are able to grow and expand along the way. We are the hero, but there are other people who help us on the journey. They can inspire the launch and encourage us to continue on. This only happens if you put yourself out there in the first place. Some people may be hesitant to share their work because they are perfectionists. That leads to procrastination or even quitting completely. Be aware of this potential roadblock on the path.

As artists, it can be tempting to constantly seek external validation for our creations. This quest must be balanced with an inner knowing. Amidst all those feelings that we have as an artist, of insecurity, doubt, and the imposter syndrome, it seems the only way through is to keep going. At least twice in my life I've received that message from my mentors. Perhaps, subliminally, that's why I'm still going. I have wanted to quit many times. But just thinking of that letter from Paul, or the words of Kaz, refuels my fire and I carry on.

One of the most valuable things you can do when you have time alone is to deepen your relationship with creativity. Nurture it, foster it, explore it and love it. Creativity is all about connecting with Divine Source, balancing the elements within and without. When we gratefully breathe the Air, drink the Water, bask in the Sun, ground ourselves in the Earth, and stay connected to Source, creativity flows like rain. Energy and purpose fuse into focused action, creating beauty and harmony in the world.

The beach is a perfect place to practice and heal in my experience. All of the elements are balanced in complete harmony. Fresh Air to breathe, sunlight (Fire) to soak in, rocks and sand (Earth) to soothe the feet, the Water waves creating the cosmic sound of OM, omnipresent, the Ether containing every melody that ever was or shall be.

Culture is not static, it is constantly evolving. As you learn and grow, your understanding of sound healing will also evolve. Allow yourself to be inspired by different traditions and cultures, but also trust your own intuition and inner guidance. You can integrate these into your own unique blend of sound healing practices. Embracing this path, you can create an experience that is relevant to your own time and place while honoring the roots of the traditions that have come before us. Ultimately, sound healing is about connecting with your own innate healing abilities and using the power of sound to support your journey towards greater health and wellbeing.

Whether you are new to sound healing or an experienced practitioner, I hope that this book has inspired you to explore the power of sound to awaken spiritual, mental, emotional, and physical wellbeing. We have explored the five elements through the lens of sound healing. We learned how to use them to create a transformative and healing experience. Take everything you have learned in this book and apply it to your practice.

All of these various tools work together to support our travels through this elemental soundscape. Ultimately, what we bring to each ceremony is our presence and good intentions. The sonic vibrations are carriers of this energy. In the quantum field, people feel your intentions. How we live each day, and deepen into our practice, can greatly influence our outer world experience. We can create powerful, transformative experiences that help us to align with our true nature and live our best lives.

Blessings on your journey.

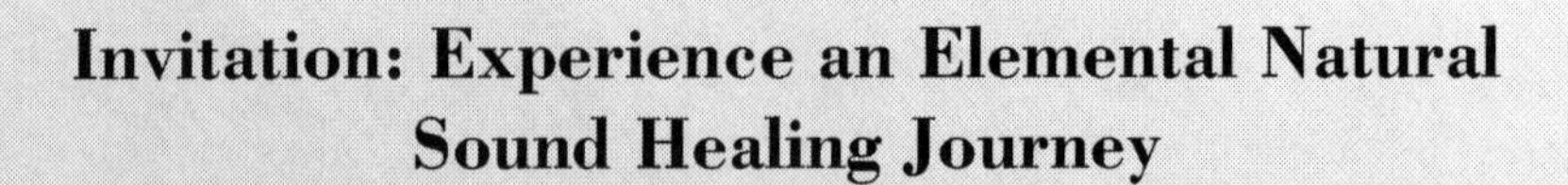

Invitation: Experience an Elemental Natural Sound Healing Journey

Sound healing, for me, is a blend of the language of nature with the language of music. If you want to experience a multi-layered, multi dimensional, natural sound healing journey, lay on the earth under the stars, dance around the fire, sit still in the wind, find a field of crickets or a pond full of frogs in the early evening, get comfortable and listen. Breathe gently and easy, focusing on the entrainment opportunities woven into the constantly changing sonic variables. Your capacity for deep listening will increase exponentially.

APPENDIX: Charts

A. Compass of 5 Elements

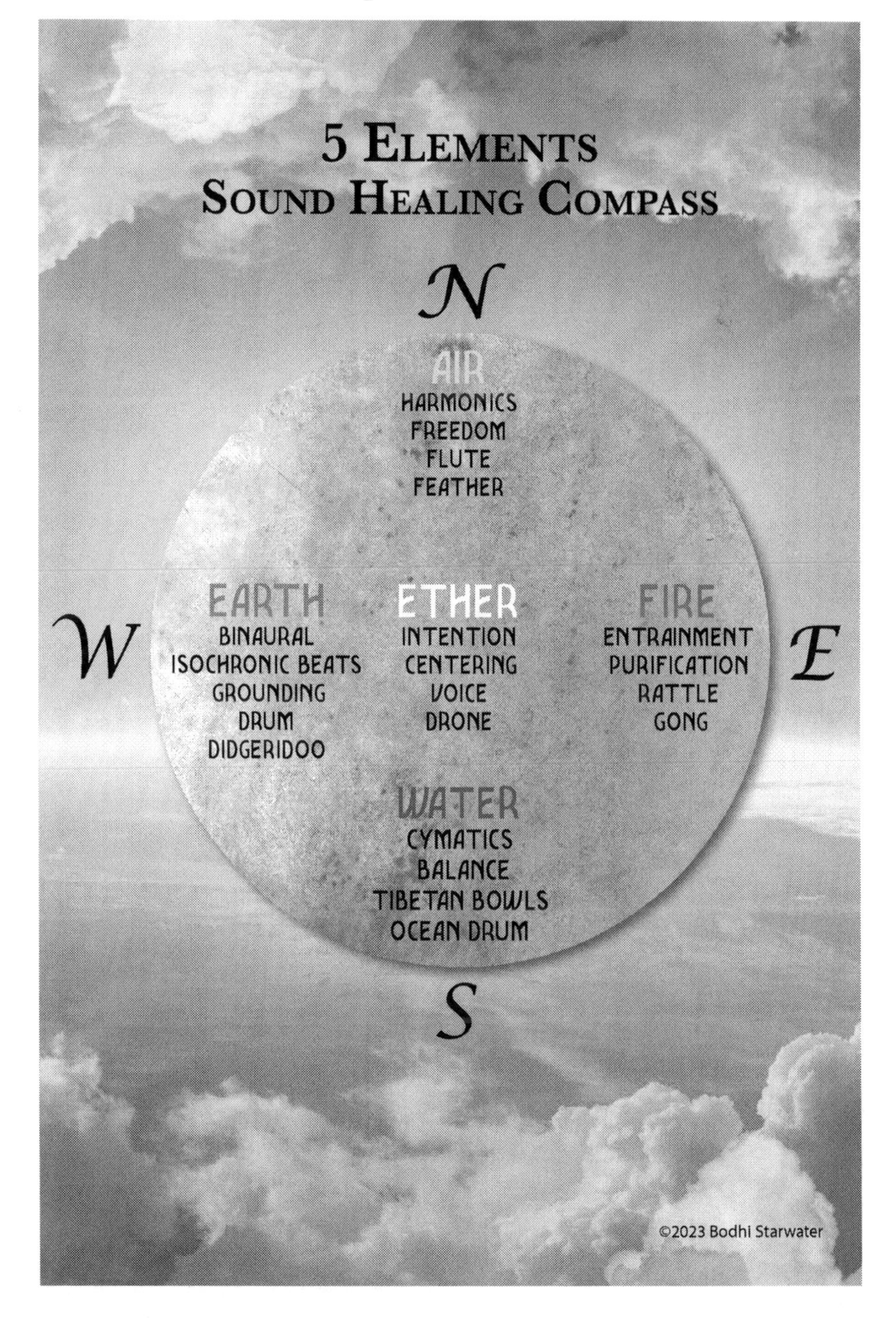

B. Table of 5 Elements

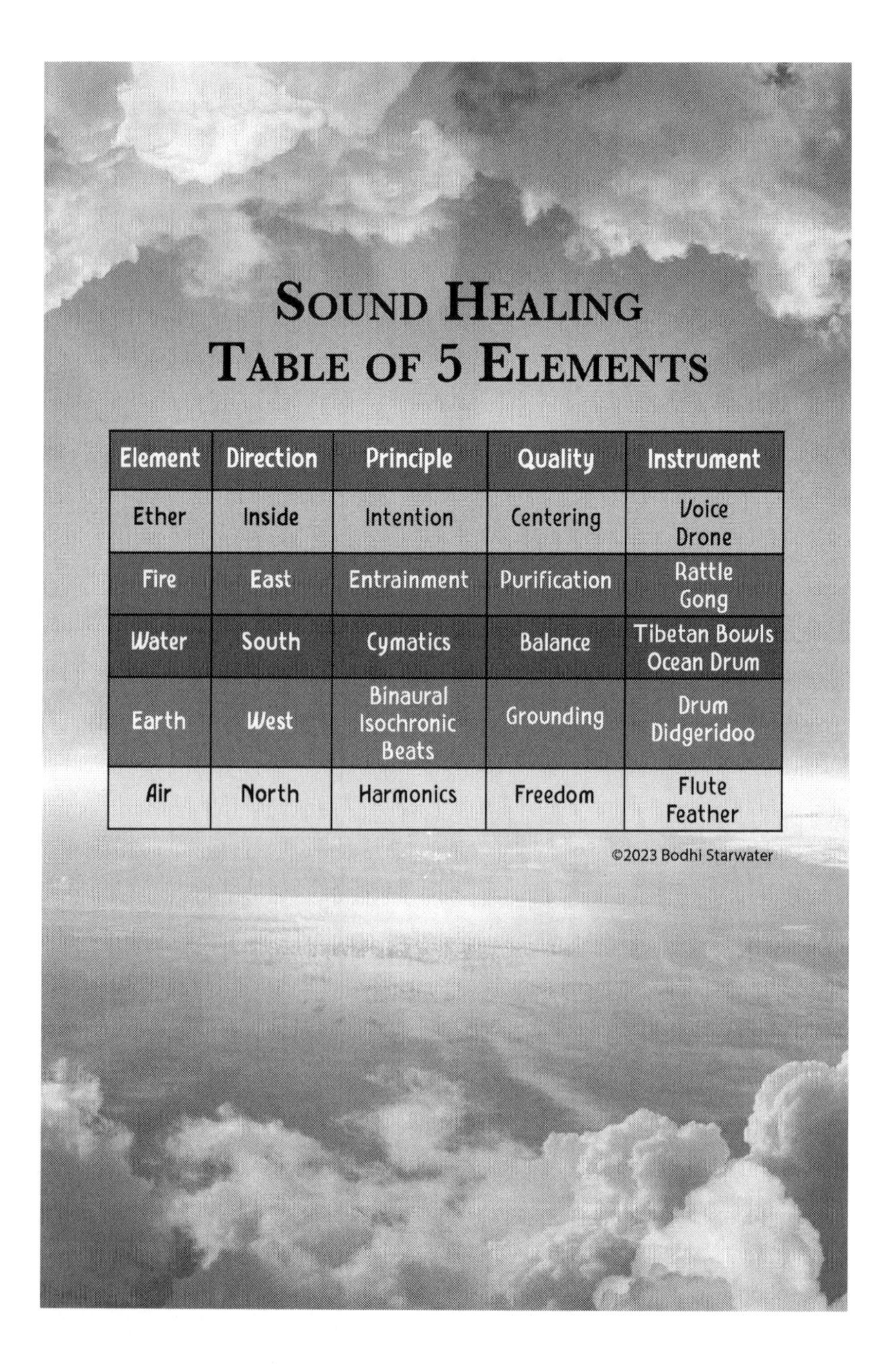

SOUND HEALING
TABLE OF 5 ELEMENTS

Element	Direction	Principle	Quality	Instrument
Ether	Inside	Intention	Centering	Voice Drone
Fire	East	Entrainment	Purification	Rattle Gong
Water	South	Cymatics	Balance	Tibetan Bowls Ocean Drum
Earth	West	Binaural Isochronic Beats	Grounding	Drum Didgeridoo
Air	North	Harmonics	Freedom	Flute Feather

C. Harmonic Overtone Series

Harmonics Overtone Series (Frequency Flowers)

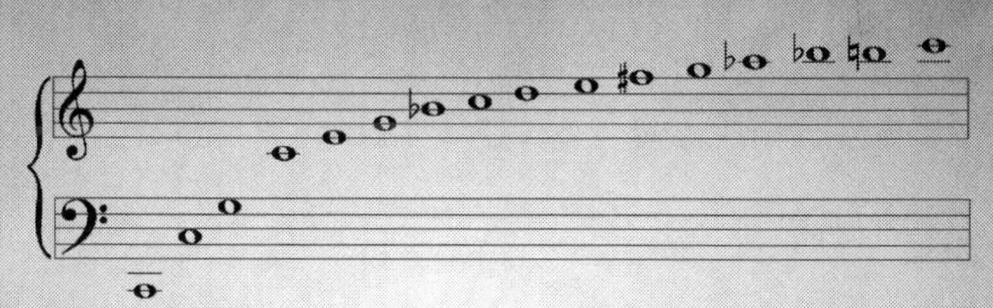

Partial	Note	Interval
1	C	Unison
2	C	Octave
3	G	Perfect 5th
4	C	Octave
5	E	Major 3rd
6	G	Perfect 5th
7	B♭	Minor 7th
8	C	Octave
9	D	Major 2nd
10	E	Major 3rd
11	F#	Augmented 4th
12	G	Perfect 5th
13	A♭	Minor 6th
14	B♭	Minor 7th
15	B	Major 7th
16	C	Octave

D. Brain Wave States

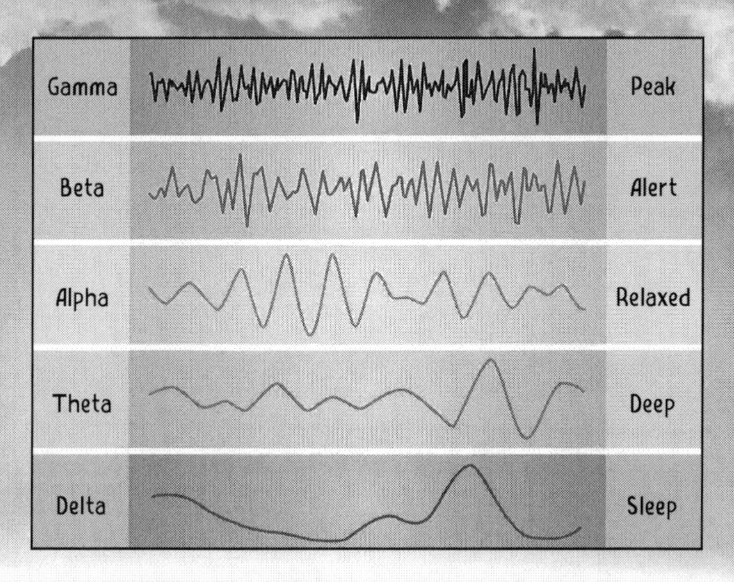

Brain Wave States	Brain Wave Frequencies	Qualities of Consciousness
Gamma	30 - 100 Hz	Insight, Peak Focus, Expanded Consciousness
Beta	13 - 30 Hz	Alertness, Concentration, Conscious thought, Stress, Anxiety, Cognition
Alpha	8 - 13 Hz	Light relaxation, Superlearning, Positive thinking, Visualization, Creativity
Theta	4 - 8 Hz	Deep relaxation, Meditation, Increased memory, Intuition, Focus, Dreams, REM sleep
Delta	.5 - 4 Hz	Deep sleep, Lucid dreaming, Healing, Increased immune functions

E. Modal Matrix

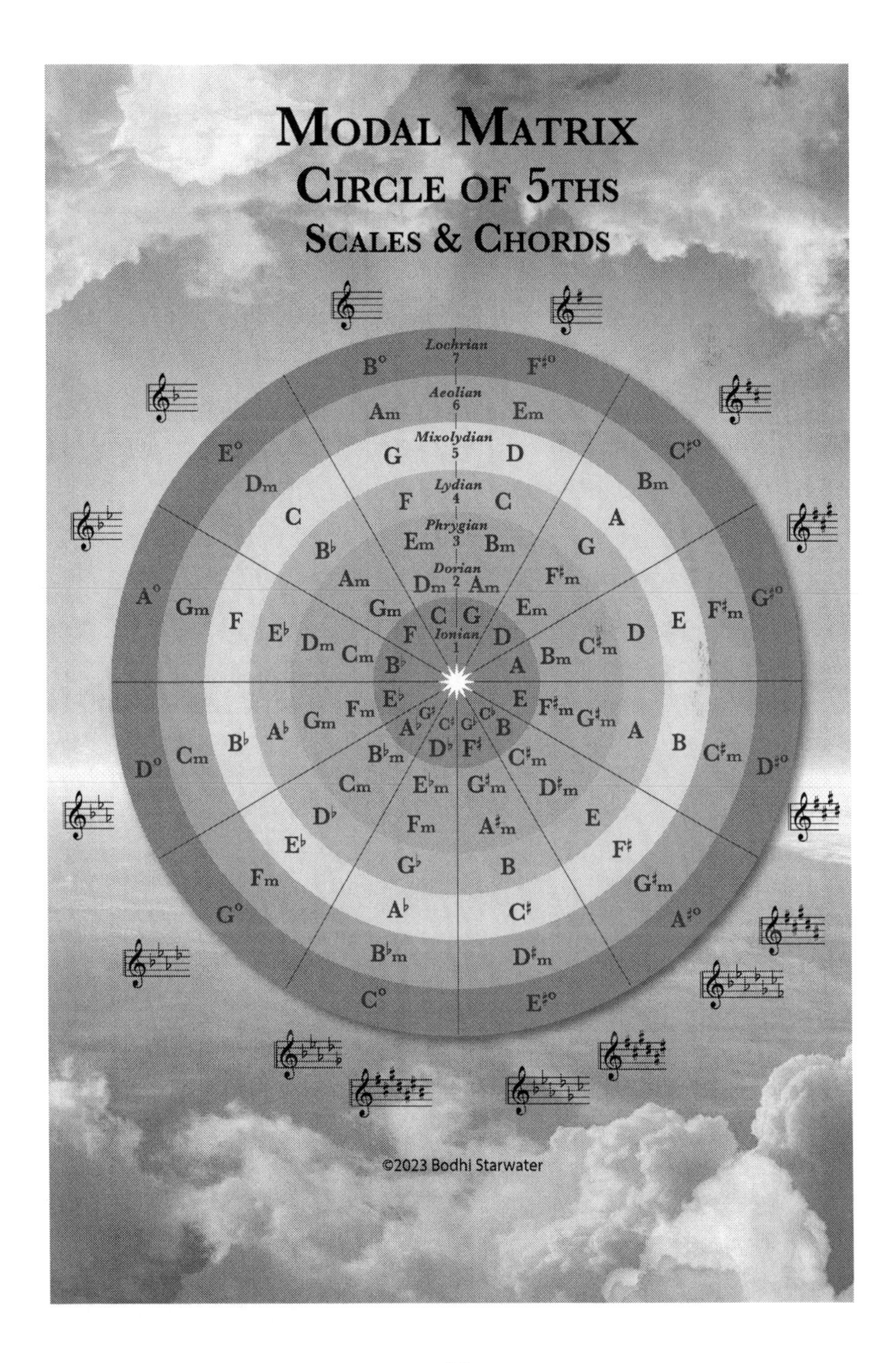

Postscript

As a final reflection, I'd like to share what a powerful, transformative journey it was to create this simple book. Organizing one's thoughts and creating a beautiful container to hold a coherent body of work is a Herculean task. For some, it might come easy. For me, it was arduous; I had to get stronger and more focused. I had to sort through my own experience to choose what was most important and relevant for me to share within the context of my personal path.

I love the diversity and different perspectives that are represented in the sound healing field. Any subjects or ideas I have omitted are covered in depth by other authors. I love teaching and hope this book will serve as a simple introduction to the way I work with sound. I look forward to continuing the conversation with you.

Finally, I am truly grateful for all the help I received along the way. I wanted to acknowledge people after you have read the book, so you might feel into the incredible knowledge and wisdom these creators hold and how much they encouraged me to finish the book.

Acknowledgments

First and foremost, I'd like to thank my teachers: Allaudin Mathieu, David Gibson, Hazrat Inayat Khan, Paul Horn, René Jenkins, Russil Paul, and Tito La Rosa. There are never enough words to completely express my gratitude for these mentors in my life.

To all my colleagues and friends, my greatest respect and appreciation for all the myriad gifts you have extended in my direction: **Aiyisha Castillo** for epic help organizing content and championing my progress; **Alvaro Congrains** for helping me in the initial organization of the elements; **Arthur Hills** for reading through the manuscript with a Masters eye; **Barbara Juniper** for reflecting my work back to me at various intervals and always encouraging me to keep going; **Brad Reynolds** for graphic design and artistic collaboration; **Christine Stevens** for invaluable suggestions along the way and writing the foreword; **Deysi Faeth** for helping me find new and captivating ways to tell my stories; **Eluña Antle** for many hours of research, conversation and co-creating on all the topics in the book; **Jasper Crocker** for photography, interview material and moral support; **Nicole Boots** for being my writing and publishing coach; **Patrick Woodworth** for a lifetime of travel, friendship and endless creative ideas; **Tarangita** for years of loving support.

SOUND (Reprise)

This portal is complete
The inner world is full
Commensurable with the outer world
Like the roots and the tree
Mirror each other

Coming from the place within
Embrace your practice with a presence of peace
This emanates forth into the space from your being

Listen to your instrument allies
Learn from them
Pay attention to their sound wisdom

Whatever is natural to you is natural for you
This is the territory to explore
We are drinking from the fountain
A container of creativity
That we have manifested together
A safe place to learn

Keep going

— Bodhi Starwater

About the Author

Bodhi Starwater Setchko is a sound healer, musician, composer, author, teacher, workshop leader, poet, creativity coach, and sonic ninja. He has a deep love of the natural world and worked for many years as a wilderness and river guide. Playing his flute in the forest, inspired by the sounds of nature, Bodhi developed his own, unique style of improvisation within the healing music modalities.

After hearing Paul Horn play the flute on the album *Inside*, recorded in the Taj Mahal, Bodhi knew at age fourteen the silver flute would be his lifelong companion. Over the years, he has added many other instruments to his orchestra, including flutes from around the world, the conch shell, charango, guitar, Tibetan bowls, feathers, keyboards, drums, and rattles.

He has studied with Tito La Rosa, Paul Horn, Allaudin Mathieu and many other artists around the globe. He has eighteen original albums in his portfolio and is the founder of performance ensembles Sonic Transfusion, Crystal Wind, and Rhythm Matrix. He has had two #1 flute albums, *Deep Dream* in 2020 and *Trans Ukraine* in 2006, on the Zone Music Reporter International New Age Music Chart. His music is used in yoga studios, health spas, and health practitioners' offices. He has had millions of plays on Spotify, Apple Music, Pandora, and other streaming sites.

In 2021, he created a Sound Healing Temple in Mt. Shasta, California, where he offers private and group sound healing journeys. He also performs for concerts, festivals, yoga classes, meditation groups, ceremonies, retreats, and conferences around the world.

BODHI
Deep Dream
SHAMANIC FLUTE JOURNEYS

BODHI
Peace Is Now
Choral Chant

BODHI
Soundscape Oasis
Sound Healing Journey
Flutes Guitar Charango Tibetan Bowls

Bodhi

BODHI
Amazing Grace
Solo Flute
Traditional Melodies

Bodhi
Inside
Flute Meditations
In A Military Bunker

HARBIN TEMPLE
BODHI

BODHI
Ocean Whispers

BODHI
Simple
NATIVE FLUTES & OCEAN WAVES

BODHI
Stillwater Canyon
A Journey Through The
SOUNDSCAPE OASIS

BODHI
Qi

Bodhi's Discography

Music avilable at: https://bodhimusic.bandcamp.com

Cloud Etchings 33
Deep Dream
Harbin Temple
Inside
Mystery
Ocean Whispers
Peace Is Now
Qi
Shamanic Flute
Simple
Soundscape Oasis
Stillwater Canyon
Trans Ukraine

Bodhi's Books

Available on Amazon Books

Tao of Music

The World is My Ashram

Bodhi Website

https://soundscapeoasiscom
Student inquires welcome

Documentary Movie

Watch on YouTube:

Bodhi Starwater: Journey of Sound and Silence

Bodhi Social Media

Amazon Music: @Bodhi

Apple Music: @Bodhi

Deezer Music: @Bodhi

Facebook: Bodhimusic

Insight Timer: @Bodhiflute

Instagram: @Bodhistarwater

Linkedin: Bodhi (Starwater) Setchko

Linktree: @Bodhistar

Pandora: @Bodhi

Patreon: @BodhiSetchko

Soundcloud: @Bodhistarwater

Spotify: @Bodhi

Tidal Music: @Bodhi

TikTok: @Bodhistarwater

Twitter: @Bodhistar

YouTube: @BodhiSoundscapeOasis

Instagram

Linktree

Spotify

Resources

My Favorite Sound Healing Music Albums:

Anugama – ***Shamanic Dream***

Brian Eno – ***Music For Airports***

Goro Yamaguchi – ***Bell Ringing In An Empty Sky***

Karma Moffet – ***Golden Bowls***

Laraji – ***Koto***

Paul Horn – ***Inside***

Russill Paul – ***The Yoga of Sound***

Tito La Rosa – ***Viaje de Curación***

Tony Scott – ***Zen Meditation***

Resources for instruments

Many of the instruments discussed in this book are available at an on-line music store called **Didge Project**

References Books

Campbell, D. (2014). *The Roar of Silence: Healing Powers of Breath, Tone and Music*. Quest Books.

Gibson, D. (2013). *The Complete Guide to Sound Healing: Physical Healing, Emotional Healing, Mental Clarity, Opening the Heart, Connecting to Spirit*.

Goldman, J., & Goldman, A. (2017). *The Humming Effect: Sound Healing for Health and Happiness*. Simon and Schuster.

Jenny, H. (2001b). *Cymatics: A Study of Wave Phenomena and Vibration*. Macromedia.

Khan, I. (1983). *The Music of Life*.

Khan, H. I. (2020). *The Sufi Message of Hazrat Inayat Khan: The Mysticism of Sound, Music, The Power of the Word, Cosmic Language*. Library of Alexandria.

Paul, R. (2006). *The Yoga of Sound: Tapping the Hidden Power of Music and Chant*. New World Library.

Perry, W. (2012). *Sound Medicine: The Complete Guide to Healing with Sound and the Human Voice*. Createspace Independent Pub.

Stevens, C. (2012). *Music medicine: The Science and Spirit of Healing Yourself with Sound*. Sounds True.

Tomatis, A. (1991). *The Conscious Ear: My Life of Transformation Through Listening*.

Underhill, R. M. (2023). *Singing for Power: The Song Magic of the Papago Indians of Southern Arizona*. Univ of California Press.

References Websites

A short history and introduction to crystal bowls. (n.d.). https://sunreed.com/a-short-history-and-introduction-to-crystal-bowls/

APA Dictionary of Psychology. (n.d.). https://dictionary.apa.org/centering

Ashar, R. (2023). Flauta nativa Ashar | Flauta nativa Ashar. *Flauta Nativa Ashar*. https://www.flautanativa.com/en/tito-la-rosa-e-a-medicina-das-flautas/

Building Beautiful Souls, Inc. (2021, July 6). *Fire Element Symbolism & Meaning | Symbols and Meanings*. https://www.buildingbeautifulsouls.com/symbols-meanings/five-elements-symbolic-meaning/fire-element-symbolic-meaning/

Carter, S. (2022, February 28). *Ancient customs of using sound therapy can lead to healing – Bluffton Sun*. Bluffton Sun. https://www.blufftonsun.com/ancient-customs-of-using-sound-therapy-can-lead-to-healing/

Centering - Definition, Meaning & Synonyms. (n.d.). In *Vocabulary.com*. https://www.vocabulary.com/dictionary/centering

Clarabut, J. (2023, March 29). *Why relaxation is so important | Wellbeing People*. Wellbeing People. https://www.wellbeingpeople.com/2019/04/15/why-relaxation-is-so-important/

Cosentino, S. (2022, August 17). *Sound Healing: the power of sound to heal, to create new life*. Crossing Worlds Journeys and Retreats. https://crossingworlds.com/sound-healing/

Definition of space. (2023). In *Merriam-Webster Dictionary*. https://www.merriam-webster.com/dictionary/space

Denver Percussion. (2019, September 25). *History of drum therapy*. https://www.denverpercussion.com/history-of-drum-therapy/#:~:text=Throughout%20the%20millennia%2C%20African%20healers,in%20Mongolia%2C%20Persia%20and%20Mesopotamia.

Didge Therapy –. (n.d.). – Didge Therapy -. http://didgetherapy.com/

Didgeridoo, vibrational medicine and sound therapy. (n.d.). X8 Drums & Percussion, Inc. https://www.x8drums.com/blog/didgeridoo-vibrational-medicine-and-sound-therapy/

Entrainment Definition and Meaning | Dictionary.com. (2021). In *Dictionary.com*. https://www.dictionary.com/browse/entrainment

Flying Legend USA. (2021). Emotion and psychology about the Flight. *Flying Legend*. https://www.flyinglegendusa.com/2021/03/25/emotion-and-psychology-about-the-flight/

Four principles of sound meditation and sound healing. (2020, December 18). Sound-meditation-sf. https://www.soundmeditationsf.com/post/four-principles-of-sound-meditation-and-sound-healing#:~:text=Instruments%20that%20are%20rich%20in,and%20profound%20effect%20on%20us.

Halpern, M. (2020). The Five Elements: Earth in Ayurveda. *California College of Ayurveda*. https://www.ayurvedacollege.com/blog/five-elements-earth-ayurveda/

How a Didgeridoo is Made – Myth and Facts. (n.d.). https://www.didjshop.com/shop1/HowDidgeridooIsMade-MythAndFacts.html

Hussein, J. (2021, November 10). It might be time for a spiritual cleansing. *Coveteur: Inside Closets, Fashion, Beauty, Health, and Travel.* https://coveteur.com/spiritual-cleansing

Idyllic Melody. (2022, April 30). *Regeneración de Tejidos Corporales (Terapia de Sonido), Rejuvenecimiento de Todo el Cuerpo* [Video]. YouTube. https://www.youtube.com/watch?v=bonF5fN4vqo

Intention – Definition, meaning & Synonyms. (n.d.). In *Vocabulary.com*. https://www.vocabulary.com/dictionary/intention

Key Step Media. (2022, January 14). What is Emotional Balance? (And How to Cultivate It) - Key Step Media. *Key Step Media - Leadership, Mindfulness, Emotional Intelligence*. https://www.keystepmedia.com/emotional-balance/#:~:text=Practices%20like%20meditation%20with%20focus,we%20can%20cultivate%20Emotional%20Balance.

Lab, S. H. (2019, May 25). The Science of Healing with Native American Flute. *Sound Healing LAB*. https://soundhealinglab.com/blogs/stories/how-our-bodies-respond-to-sounds-of-native-american-flute

Libretexts. (2023). 2.2: Human voice as instrument. *Humanities LibreTexts*. https://human.libretexts.org/Bookshelves/Music/Book%3A_Music_-_Its_Language_History_and_Culture_(Cohen)/02%3A_Musical_Instruments_and_Ensembles/2.02%3A_Human_Voice_as_Instrument

Living Well. (2019, September 12). *Grounding exercises – Living Well.* Living Well – a Resource for Men Who Have Been Sexually Abused or Sexually Assaulted, for Partners, Family and Friends and for Professionals. https://

livingwell.org.au/well-being/mental-health/grounding-exercises/

MasterClass. (2020, November 8). *A Brief History of Drums: On the Origin of Percussion – 2023 – MasterClass*. https://www.masterclass.com/articles/a-brief-history-of-drums

Nature. (n.d.). https://www.soundtravels.co.uk/p-Chacapa_Reeds-7134.aspx#:~:text=Chacapa%20%E2%80%93%20also%20known%20as%20Shakapa,fronds%2C%20tobacco%2C%20and%20songs.

Newlyn, E. (2021). Journey through the 5 elements: Water. *Ekhart Yoga*. https://www.ekhartyoga.com/articles/practice/5-elements-water

Newlyn, E. (2023). Journey through the 5 elements: Ether. *Ekhart Yoga*. https://www.ekhartyoga.com/articles/philosophy/journey-through-the-5-elements-ether#:~:text=Referred%20to%20as%20'akasha'%20in,most%20subtle%20of%20all%20elements.

Pappas, S. (2016). 7 bizarre ancient cultures that history forgot. *livescience.com*. https://www.livescience.com/55430-bizarre-ancient-cultures.html

Paros, J. (2021). What does freedom feel like? Unconditional permission to live – author. *Author*. https://www.authormagazine.org/articles/2021/8/paros

Psychology, P. (2022). Psychological space (Definition + benefits). *Practical Psychology*. https://practicalpie.com/psychological-space/

Purification Definition & Meaning | Dictionary.com. (2020). In *Dictionary.com*. https://www.dictionary.com/browse/purification

Rhythmtherapy. (2013, June 22). *Drum types and origins: The Ocean Drum*. The Rhythm. https://drummingtherapy.

wordpress.com/2013/06/22/drum-types-and-origins-the-ocean-drum/

Rizzi, S. (2023). Hear the world's oldest instrument, the 50,000 year old neanderthal flute. *Classic FM*. https://www.classicfm.com/discover-music/instruments/flute/worlds-oldest-instrument-neanderthal-flute/

SecretStaff. (2021). How to Create Your Life With The Power of Intention. *The Official Website of the Secret*. https://www.thesecret.tv/blog/the-power-of-intention/#:~:text=We%20can%20use%20our%20free,are%20intending%20your%20future%20life.

Seladi-Schulman, J., PhD. (2020, February 28). *Do isochronic tones have real health benefits?* Healthline. https://www.healthline.com/health/isochronic-tones

Shaman's rattle | Tsimshian, Native American | The Metropolitan Museum of Art. (n.d.). The Metropolitan Museum of Art. https://www.metmuseum.org/art/collection/search/717586

Soundhealing.gr. (2022, October 15). *Sound Healing: Everything you need to know - Soundhealing.gr*. https://www.soundhealing.gr/soundhealing/

Staff, & Staff. (2023). Native American Drums: A brief history of the early instruments. *Drumming Review*. https://drummingreview.com/native-american-drums/

Staff, M. (n.d.). *MacProVideo.com*. macProVideo.com. https://macprovideo.com/article/audio-hardware/how-sound-affects-you-gongs-in-sound-therapy

The Air Element – The Wiccan Elements – Wicca Living. (2017, November 6). Wicca Living. https://wiccaliving.com/air-element/

The Earth Element – The Wiccan Elements – Wicca Living. (2017,

November 6). Wicca Living. https://wiccaliving.com/earth-element/

The Editors of Encyclopedia Britannica. (1998, July 20). *PanPipe | Andean, Peruvian & Bolivian*. Encyclopedia Britannica. https://www.britannica.com/art/panpipe

The Editors of Encyclopedia Britannica. (2023, September 15). *Resonance | Frequency, amplitude & wavelength*. Encyclopedia Britannica. https://www.britannica.com/science/resonance-vibration

The Use Of Harmonies In Therapeutic Sound Healing. (n.d.). https://sunreed.com/the-use-of-harmonies-in-therapeutic-sound-healing/

Verma, P. (2021, December 11). This is what true freedom feels like - ascent publication - medium. *Medium*. https://medium.com/the-ascent/this-is-what-true-freedom-feels-like-c8a0e425fcaa#:~:text=It's%20the%20emotional%20and%20spiritual,is%20not%20under%20your%20control.

Wagner, B. B., Wagner, B. B., & Wagner, B. B. (2019). Primeval communication and the beat of the drum. *Ancient Origins Reconstructing the Story of Humanity's Past*. https://www.ancient-origins.net/history-ancient-traditions/drum-0012677

What is musical entrainment? (2016, December 9). Music & Science Lab. https://musicscience.net/projects/timing/iemp/what-is-musical-entrainment/

What is Sound Healing. (n.d.). The College of Sound Healing. https://www.collegeofsoundhealing.co.uk/what_is.php

What is the difference between "clearing" and "cleansing" ? "clearing" vs "leansing" ? (2023, April 20). HiNative. https://hinative.com/questions/5323027

Why Does Experiencing 'Flow' Feel So Good? (2022, January 12). UC Davis. https://www.ucdavis.edu/curiosity/blog/research-shows-people-who-have-flow-regular-part-their-lives-are-happier-and-less-likely-focus

Wikipedia contributors. (2023). Aether (classical element). *Wikipedia*. https://en.wikipedia.org/wiki/Aether_(classical_element)

Wikipedia contributors. (2023a). Air (classical element). *Wikipedia*. https://en.wikipedia.org/wiki/Air_(classical_element)

Wikipedia contributors. (2023a). Intention. *Wikipedia*. https://en.wikipedia.org/wiki/Intention

Wikipedia contributors. (2023a). Isochronic tones. *Wikipedia*. https://en.wikipedia.org/wiki/Isochronic_tones

Wikipedia contributors. (2023a). Ocean drum. *Wikipedia*. https://en.wikipedia.org/wiki/Ocean_drum#:~:text=2%20Playing-,History,by%20a%20Parisian%20instrument%20maker.

Wikipedia contributors. (2023a). Water drum. *Wikipedia*. https://en.wikipedia.org/wiki/Water_drum

Wikipedia contributors. (2023b). Earth (classical element). *Wikipedia*. https://en.wikipedia.org/wiki/Earth_(classical_element)

Wikipedia contributors. (2023b). Fire (classical element). *Wikipedia*. https://en.wikipedia.org/wiki/Fire_(classical_element)

Wikipedia contributors. (2023b). Paleolithic flute. *Wikipedia*. https://en.wikipedia.org/wiki/Paleolithic_flute

Wikipedia contributors. (2023c). Water (classical element). *Wikipedia*. https://en.wikipedia.org/wiki/Water_(classical_element)

Wikipedia contributors. (2023e). Resonance. *Wikipedia*. https://en.wikipedia.org/wiki/Resonance

Wind instrument | Classifications, History, & Facts. (1999, July 26). Encyclopedia Britannica. https://www.britannica.com/art/wind-instrument/Flutes

Z, S. (2018, July 2). *The Healing Powers Of Shamanic Drumming –7th Sense Stories*. 7th Sense Stories. https://www.7thsensepsychics.com/stories/the-healing-powers-of-shamanic-drumming/

Notes

Notes

Notes

Notes

Notes

Where

the music

goes

Sound Healing Temple in Mt Shasta, CA

Quantum Sound Healing Experience

soundscapeoasis.com

CWP

Made in the USA
Columbia, SC
30 July 2024